Test Bank for

Elementary Algebra

Mugridge

Test Questions by
Mary Chabot,
Mt. San Antonio College
and
IPS Publishing

SAUNDERS COLLEGE PUBLISHING
Philadelphia   Fort Worth   Chicago
San Francisco   Montreal   Toronto
London   Sydney   Tokyo

Mugridge: Test Bank for ELEMENTARY ALGEBRA

ISBN # 0-03-009414-3

012 095 987654321

PREFACE

This Printed Test Bank contains test questions generated from the Apple and IBM versions of the Computerized Test Bank that accompanies Mugridge, ELEMENTARY ALGEBRA. The Test Bank can be used as a source of all of the questions on the disks; it can also be used in place of the disks for those who do not have access to a computer. The pages are perforated and the answers are listed separately so that the tests can be torn out and duplicated for your students.

The Apple version of the Test Bank (pp. 1 - 277 of this manual) contains 1200 questions, both open-ended and multiple choice. This copy was generated from ExaMaster, which is described on page iv. There are 100 questions for each chapter of the text; the answers are grouped together following the questions. For each question we have provided information on the level of difficulty, whether it is a short answer or multiple choice question, and the section and objective number in the text where this type of question can be found. If you would like to create your own tests from the software, it is available free to adopters by calling your Saunders sales representative.

The IBM version of the Test Bank (pp. 279 - 370 of this manual) was generated by TestMaker III. This is an algorithm-based system, which allows the instructor to create many unique tests. We have generated one test for each chapter of the text and included it in this manual. TestMaker is described on page 278 and is also available from your Saunders sales representative.

If you have any comments or suggestions about this Test Bank, please address them to: Mathematics Editor, Saunders College Publishing, The Curtis Center, Independence Square West, Philadelphia, Pennsylvania 19106-3399.

ExaMaster

ExaMaster is a computerized test preparation system designed for use with textbooks. ExaMaster is designed so that you do not need computer expertise to use it: you can focus your attention instead on test construction. All that you will need to know is explained in the User's Guide that is packaged with the disk. If you have any questions, you can call our Software Support Analyst, Kathy Jones, at (817) 334-7701.

With ExaMaster, you can:

1. Quickly create and print a test containing any combination of questions from the set of test questions accompanying your textbook.

2. Choose test questions in three ways: by chapter and question number, by viewing each question on the screen, or by random selection (according to difficulty level, learning objective, question type, or other criteria).

3. Add your own questions and answers of any length or type (e.g., multiple choice, true-false, matching, fill-in-the-blank, or essay).

4. Edit the questions and answers already provided.

5. Create a test covering one or more chapters of the book.

6. Print scrambled versions of the same test.

7. Include subscripts, superscripts, and special symbols in the test questions.

CHAPTER 1:   OPERATIONS AND VARIABLES

SHORT ANSWER

1. Write in lowest terms:

   14/63

2. Write in lowest terms:

   154/88

3. Find the product (answer in lowest terms):

   $$\left(\frac{2}{3}\right) \quad \left(\frac{21}{4}\right) \quad \left(\frac{3}{14}\right)$$

4. Find the product (answer in lowest terms):

   $$\left(\frac{12}{105}\right) \quad \left(\frac{35}{22}\right) \quad \left(\frac{21}{27}\right)$$

5. Find the quotient (answer in lowest terms):

   $(24/5) \div (15/8)$

6. Perform the indicated operations (answer in lowest terms):

   $$\left(\frac{3}{7} \cdot 21\right) \div \frac{2}{3}$$

7. Perform the indicated operations (answer in lowest terms):

   $$\frac{5}{12} + \frac{2}{3} - \frac{1}{6}$$

8. A rectangle has two sides which are each $2\frac{1}{5}$ feet long and the other two sides are each $3\frac{1}{3}$ feet long. Find the total distance around the rectangle (answer as a reduced mixed numeral).

9. Perform the indicated operations (answer in lowest terms):

   $$\frac{1}{9} + \frac{4}{9} - \frac{2}{9}$$

10. Write the following expression in words:

    $2(9-y)$

11. Write the following statement using symbols: "the quotient of w and 8 is equal to the difference of w and 5."

12. Find the value of 3^4

13. Simplify:

$6 + 2 \cdot 5$

14. Simplify:

$12 - 2 \cdot 4 + 6 \div 2$

15. Simplify:

$[\ 50 - (2 + 3^2)\ ]\ (6 - 4)^3$

16. Find the absolute value of -13

17. $|\ -0.135\ | =$

18. Place either < or > between the two numbers to make the statement true:

$0.502 \qquad 0.53$

19. Place either < or > between the two numbers to make the statement true:

$\dfrac{5}{3} \qquad \dfrac{11}{7}$

20. On the above number line, graph:

$\left[\ -\dfrac{1}{3},\ -4.75,\ \dfrac{11}{2}\ \right]$

21. Represent the quantity as either a positive number or a negative number:

"During the night, the temperature dropped 12 degrees."

22. Find the additive inverse of $-\dfrac{3}{11}$

23. Simplify:

$6 + (-13) + (-9 + 11)$

24. Simplify:

$|\ 4 + (-7)\ | - (-20)$

3

25. Simplify:

$$\frac{5}{9} - \frac{5}{6}$$

26. Simplify:

$$-5.2 - 3.15$$

27. Subtract -6 from -20

28. $| 5 - 9 | - | -6 | =$

29. Simplify:

$$23 - (5 - 14)$$

30. Simplify:

$$(-36) + (+17) + (-40)$$

31. Find the product (answer in lowest terms):

$$\left(-\frac{3}{7} \right) \left(\frac{14}{9} \right)$$

32. Multiply:

$$(-30) \ (-5)$$

33. Find the reciprocal of 14

34. Find the quotient:

$$-\frac{16}{9} \div 12$$

35. Simplify:

$$\frac{-2 - 16}{9 - 11}$$

36. Jana bought five bags of potatoes. How many pounds of potatoes did she buy if each bag contains 8.3 pounds?

37. Simplify (answer in lowest terms):

$$\frac{| 6 - 19 | - 5^2}{-3 - 5}$$

38. Find the value of $5 - 6^2$

39. Evaluate $5x^2 - 3y + 1$, if $x = 2$ and $y = -10$

40. Evaluate $x^2 - (y + 2)^2 - 14$, if $x = -2$ and $y = -5$

41. Write an algebraic expression for:

    "Six less than three times a number y."

42. Write the following sentence as an equation, using x as a variable (do not solve):

    "The quotient of 12 and the square of a number is 14."

43. Determine solutions of $x^2 - 12 = x$ from the set $\{0, 2, 4\}$

44. Use the associative property of addition to simplify:

    $5 + (8 + 2x)$

45. Use the distributive property to simplify:

    $3(5 - 2x)$

46. Simplify:

    $3(y + 4) - 17$

47. Simplify:

    $0.8 - 0.4 (x + 3) + 2$

48. Each truck in a nine-truck convoy is carrying 2000 pounds of bananas and 1200 pounds of tangerines. How much produce is being transported by the convoy?

49. State the property that is being illustrated:

    $6 + (x + 3) = 6 + (3 + x)$

50. State the property that is being illustrated:

    $(5)(3x) = (5 \cdot 3)(x)$

5

MULTIPLE CHOICE

51. Write in lowest terms:

$$\frac{18}{24}$$

   a. $\frac{2}{3}$

   b. $\frac{3}{4}$

   c. $\frac{5}{6}$

   d. $\frac{9}{12}$

   e. none of these

52. Write in lowest terms:

$$\frac{42}{105}$$

   a. $\frac{14}{35}$

   b. $\frac{6}{25}$

   c. $\frac{2}{5}$

   d. $\frac{3}{5}$

   e. none of these

53. Find the product (answer in lowest terms):

$$\left(\frac{4}{9}\right) \left(\frac{11}{8}\right) \left(\frac{36}{55}\right)$$

a. $\frac{2}{5}$

b. $\frac{3}{5}$

c. $\frac{44}{55}$

d. $\frac{44}{110}$

e. none of these

54. Find the quotient (answer in lowest terms):

$$\frac{75}{32} \div \frac{9}{10}$$

a. $\frac{135}{64}$

b. $\frac{125}{48}$

c. $\frac{225}{64}$

d. $\frac{75}{48}$

e. none of these

55. Mike drank $\frac{1}{5}$ of a pitcher of lemonade and Leon drank $\frac{1}{4}$ of the pitcher. How much lemonade is left?

    a. $\frac{1}{9}$ of the pitcher

    b. $\frac{7}{9}$ of the pitcher

    c. $\frac{9}{20}$ of the pitcher

    d. $\frac{11}{20}$ of the pitcher

    e. none of these

56. Perform the indicated operations (answer in lowest terms):

$$\left[\frac{5}{9} \cdot 12\right] \div \frac{3}{4}$$

    a. $\frac{1}{5}$

    b. 5

    c. $\frac{20}{3}$

    d. $\frac{80}{3}$

    e. none of these

57. Perform the indicated operations (answer in lowest terms):

$$\frac{5}{18} + \frac{7}{9} - \frac{2}{3}$$

    a. $\frac{7}{18}$

    b. $\frac{5}{13}$

    c. $\frac{5}{6}$

    d. $\frac{7}{6}$

    e. none of these

58. A cake recipe calls for $1\frac{1}{3}$ cups of sugar and a pie recipe calls for $\frac{3}{4}$ of a cup of sugar. If Yolanda wants to bake both the cake and the pie, how much sugar will she need?

a. $1\frac{4}{7}$ cups

b. $2\frac{1}{2}$ cups

c. $2\frac{1}{12}$ cups

d. 1 cup

e. none of these

59. Perform the indicated operations (answer in lowest terms):

$$\frac{2}{15} + \frac{8}{15} - \frac{7}{15}$$

a. $\frac{1}{3}$

b. $\frac{1}{15}$

c. $\frac{2}{5}$

d. $\frac{4}{15}$

e. none of these

60. Write the following expression in words:

$$2\left(\frac{15}{y}\right)$$

a. twice the sum of 15 and y
b. twice the product of 15 and y
c. the square of the product of 15 and y
d. twice the quotient of 15 and y
e. none of these

61. Write the following statement using symbols:

"The difference of 6 and t is equal to the product of 9 and t."

a. $6 + t = 9 + t$
b. $6 - t = 9 + t$
c. $6 - t = 9t$
d. $6 + t = 9t$
e. none of these

62. Find the value of 5^3

a. 15
b. 75
c. 35
d. 125
e. none of these

63. Simplify:

$$15 - 5 \cdot 2$$

a. 5
b. 20
c. 40
d. 10
e. none of these

64. Simplify:

$$16 + 4 \div 2 + 3 \cdot 5$$

a. 25
b. 20
c. 105
d. 33
e. none of these

65. Simplify:

$$[80 - (3 + 5)^2] (30 - 3^3)$$

a. 48
b. 432
c. 132
d. 336
e. none of these

66. Find the absolute value of -25

    a. -25
    b. 25
    c. -5
    d. 5
    e. none of these

67. $\left| -\dfrac{5}{9} \right| =$

    a. $-\dfrac{5}{9}$

    b. $\dfrac{5}{9}$

    c. $\dfrac{9}{5}$

    d. $-\dfrac{9}{5}$

    e. none of these

68. Write in order from smallest to largest:

        2.3, 2.12, 2.04

    a. {2.3, 2.04, 2.12}
    b. {2.04, 2.3, 2.12}
    c. {2.04, 2.12, 2.3}
    d. {2.3, 2.12, 2.04}
    e. none of these

69. Write in order from smallest to largest:

    $\dfrac{7}{3}, \dfrac{9}{5}, \dfrac{12}{7}$

    a. $\left[\dfrac{12}{7}, \dfrac{9}{5}, \dfrac{7}{3} \right]$

    b. $\left[\dfrac{9}{5}, \dfrac{7}{3}, \dfrac{12}{7} \right]$

    c. $\left[\dfrac{9}{5}, \dfrac{12}{7}, \dfrac{7}{3} \right]$

    d. $\left[\dfrac{7}{3}, \dfrac{9}{5}, \dfrac{12}{7} \right]$

    e. none of these

a.

b.

c.

d.

e.

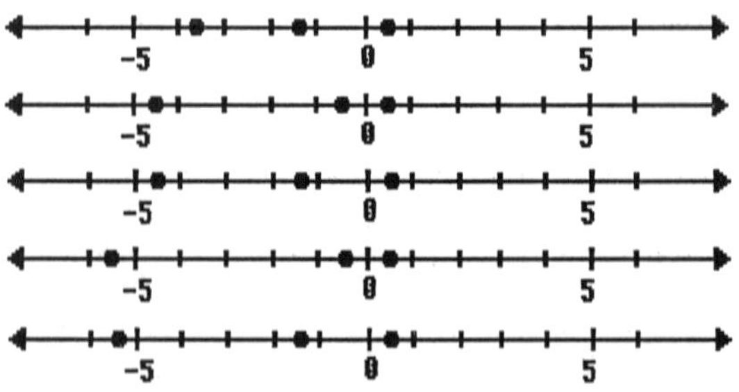

70. Which of the above graphs is a correct graph of:

$$\left[\frac{1}{2}, -\frac{4}{3}, -4.75 \right] ?$$

71. Use signed numbers to represent the following: "the temperature rose 8 degrees during the day, then dropped 12 degrees that night."

    a. (+8) + (+12)
    b. (−8) + (−12)
    c. (+8) + (−12)
    d. (−8) + (+12)
    e. none of these

72. Find the additive inverse of $-\frac{5}{12}$

    a. $-\frac{12}{5}$

    b. $\frac{12}{5}$

    c. $-\frac{5}{12}$

    d. $\frac{5}{12}$

    e. none of these

73. Simplify:

    8 + (−21) + (−15 + 6)

    a. 20
    b. −4
    c. 22
    d. 4
    e. none of these

12

74. Simplify:

$$| 6 + (-11) | - | 23 - 25 |$$

a. -33
b. 3
c. 7
d. 19
e. none of these

75. Simplify (answer in lowest terms):

$$\frac{1}{8} - \frac{1}{6}$$

a. $\frac{1}{2}$

b. $\frac{1}{24}$

c. $-\frac{1}{24}$

d. $\frac{1}{48}$

e. none of these

76. Simplify:

$$-6.3 - 2.19$$

a. -8.22
b. -4.11
c. -8.11
d. -8.49
e. none of these

77. Subtract -4 from -15

a. -11
b. -19
c. 11
d. 19
e. none of these

78. $| 16 - 23 | - | 9 - 11 | =$

a. -5
b. 9
c. 19
d. 41
e. none of these

79. Simplify:

$$(53 - 60) - (3 - 8)$$

a. 2
b. −12
c. −2
d. −4
e. none of these

80. Simplify:

$$(-49) + (+36) + (-8)$$

a. −5
b. −21
c. −93
d. −77
e. none of these

81. Find the product (answer in lowest terms):

$$\left(-\frac{9}{14}\right)\left(\frac{21}{22}\right)$$

a. $-\frac{3}{11}$

b. $-\frac{27}{154}$

c. $-\frac{189}{308}$

d. $-\frac{27}{22}$

e. none of these

82. Multiply:

$$(-0.3)(5)$$

a. 1.5
b. −1.5
c. 0.15
d. −0.15
e. none of these

83. Find the reciprocal of $\frac{2}{11}$

    a. $-\frac{2}{11}$

    b. $-\frac{11}{2}$

    c. $\frac{11}{2}$

    d. $\frac{2}{11}$

    e.   none of these

84. Find the quotient:

$$-\frac{25}{8} \div 10$$

    a. $\frac{5}{16}$

    b. $-\frac{5}{16}$

    c. $\frac{125}{4}$

    d. $-\frac{125}{4}$

    e.   none of these

85. Simplify:

$$3 - 5 [5(-2) - 3(-7)]$$

    a.   -22
    b.   62
    c.   158
    d.   -52
    e.   none of these

86. A coach wishes to divide a $\frac{2}{3}$ of a mile race track into 6 equal pieces. How long will each piece be?

    a. 4 miles

    b. 9 miles

    c. $\frac{1}{9}$ of a mile

    d. $\frac{1}{4}$ of a mile

    e. none of these

87. Simplify:

$$\frac{|\ 8 - 11\ | - 9^2}{2 - 4}$$

    a. -42
    b. 42
    c. -13
    d. 39
    e. none of these

88. Find the value of $2 - 5^2$

    a. 9
    b. -23
    c. 27
    d. -9
    e. none of these

89. Evaluate $2x^2 + 5xy - 3$, if $x = 5$ and $y = -2$

    a. 47
    b. -33
    c. -3
    d. 147
    e. none of these

90. Evaluate $-b + 8ac$, if $a = 12$, $b = 5$, $c = -\frac{1}{4}$

    a. -29
    b. 29
    c. -19
    d. 19
    e. none of these

91. Write an algebraic expression for:

"Five less than the product of nine and w."

    a. 5 - 9w
    b. 9w - 5
    c. (9 + w) - 5
    d. 5 _< 9w
    e. none of these

92. Write the following sentence as an equation, using x as a variable (do not solve): "The square of the quotient of three and M is 20."

    a. 2(3 + M) = 20
    b. (3 + M)² = 20
    c. 2(3 ÷ M) = 20
    d. (3 ÷ M)² = 20
    e. none of these

93. Determine the solutions of $3x^2 + 2 = 7x$ from the set {0, 1, 2, 3}

    a. 0
    b. 1
    c. 2
    d. 3
    e. none of these

94. Use the associative property of addition to simplify:

    9 + (3 + 4x)

    a. 9 + 7x
    b. 12 + 4x
    c. 16x
    d. 3 + 13x
    e. none of these

95. Use the distributive property to simplify:

    -2(3 - 9x)

    a. -6 - 9x
    b. -6 - 18x
    c. -5 + 11x
    d. -6 + 18x
    e. none of these

96. Simplify:

   $$5(y - 2) + 3$$

   a. 5y + 1
   b. 5y + 7
   c. 5y + 13
   d. -2y
   e. none of these

97. Simplify:

   $$2.3 - 0.3(y - 2) + 1$$

   a. 2y - 3
   b. 3.9 - 0.3y
   c. 2.7 - 0.3y
   d. 1.3 - 0.3y
   e. none of these

98. One ounce of breakfast cereal contains 5 grams of protein, while four ounces of milk contains 4 grams of protein. If Shawn's daily breakfast consists of one ounce of cereal and four ounces of milk, how many grams of protein will Shawn intake at breakfast in one week?

   a. 21 grams
   b. 147 grams
   c. 39 grams
   d. 63 grams
   e. none of these

99. State the property that is being illustrated:

   $$16 + (x + 30) = (x + 30) + 16$$

   a. associative property of addition
   b. commutative property of addition
   c. distributive property
   d. additive inverse property
   e. none of these

100. State the property that is being illustrated:

   $$5 \cdot (9 + w) = (9 + w) \cdot 5$$

   a. associative property of multiplication
   b. associative property of addition
   c. commutative property of multiplication
   d. commutative property of addition
   e. none of these

1. ANS:2/9 TYPE:S DIFF:2 SECT:101 OBJ:101 RAND:Y

2. TYPE:S DIFF:3 SECT:101 OBJ:101 RAND:Y

ANSWER:
$7/4$ or $1\frac{3}{4}$

3. ANS:3/4 TYPE:S DIFF:2 SECT:101 OBJ:102 RAND:Y

4. ANS:14/99 TYPE:S DIFF:3 SECT:101 OBJ:102 RAND:Y

5. TYPE:S DIFF:1 SECT:101 OBJ:102 RAND:Y

ANSWER:
$64/25$ or $2\frac{14}{25}$

6. TYPE:S DIFF:2 SECT:101 OBJ:102 RAND:Y

ANSWER:
$27/2$ or $13\frac{1}{2}$

7. TYPE:S DIFF:2 SECT:101 OBJ:104 RAND:Y

ANSWER:
$\frac{11}{12}$

8. TYPE:S DIFF:3 SECT:101 OBJ:104 RAND:Y

ANSWER:
$11\frac{1}{15}$ feet

9. TYPE:S DIFF:1 SECT:101 OBJ:103 RAND:Y

ANSWER:
$\frac{1}{3}$

10. TYPE:S DIFF:2 SECT:102 OBJ:105 RAND:Y

ANSWER:
    Twice the difference of 9 and y

11. TYPE:S DIFF:2 SECT:102 OBJ:106 RAND:Y

ANSWER:
    $w \div 8 = w - 5$ or $\frac{w}{8} = w - 5$

12. ANS:81 TYPE:S DIFF:1 SECT:102 OBJ:105 RAND:Y

13. ANS:16 TYPE:S DIFF:1 SECT:102 OBJ:107 RAND:Y

14. ANS:7 TYPE:S DIFF:2 SECT:102 OBJ:107 RAND:Y

15. ANS:312 TYPE:S DIFF:3 SECT:102 OBJ:107 RAND:Y

16. ANS:13 TYPE:S DIFF:1 SECT:103 OBJ:110 RAND:Y

17. TYPE:S DIFF:1 SECT:103 OBJ:110 RAND:Y

18. ANS:< TYPE:S DIFF:2 SECT:103 OBJ:111 RAND:Y

19. ANS:> TYPE:S DIFF:2 SECT:103 OBJ:111 RAND:Y

20. TYPE:S DIFF:1 SECT:103 OBJ:108 GRAPH FORMAT:G
    QUESTION GRAPH:1 ANSWER GRAPH:2 RAND:Y

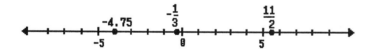

21. ANS:-12 TYPE:S DIFF:1 SECT:103 OBJ:109 RAND:Y

22. TYPE:S DIFF:1 SECT:104 OBJ:113 RAND:Y

ANSWER:
    $\frac{3}{11}$

20

23. ANS:-5   TYPE:S DIFF:2 SECT:104   OBJ:112   RAND:Y

24. ANS:23 TYPE:S DIFF:3 SECT:104   OBJ:114   RAND:Y

25. TYPE:S DIFF:3 SECT:104   OBJ:114   RAND:Y

ANSWER:
$$-\frac{5}{18}$$

26. ANS:-8.35 TYPE:S DIFF:2 SECT:104   OBJ:114   RAND:Y

27. ANS:-14 TYPE:S DIFF:2 SECT:104   OBJ:115   RAND:Y

28. ANS:-2 TYPE:S DIFF:3 SECT:104   OBJ:114   RAND:Y

29. ANS:32 TYPE:S DIFF:2 SECT:104   OBJ:114   RAND:Y

30. ANS:-59 TYPE:S DIFF:1 SECT:104   OBJ:112   RAND:Y

31. TYPE:S DIFF:1 SECT:105   OBJ:116   RAND:Y

ANSWER:
$$-\frac{2}{3}$$

32. ANS:150 TYPE:S DIFF:1 SECT:105   OBJ:116   RAND:Y

33. TYPE:S DIFF:1 SECT:105   OBJ:118   RAND:Y

ANSWER:
$$\frac{1}{14}$$

34. TYPE:S DIFF:2 SECT:105   OBJ:116   RAND:Y

ANSWER:
$$-\frac{4}{27}$$

35. ANS:9 TYPE:S DIFF:2 SECT:105   OBJ:116   RAND:Y

36. TYPE:S DIFF:2 SECT:105 OBJ:117 RAND:Y

ANSWER:
    41.5 pounds

37. TYPE:S DIFF:3 SECT:105 OBJ:116 RAND:Y

ANSWER:
    $\frac{3}{2}$ or $1\frac{1}{2}$

38. ANS:-31 TYPE:S DIFF:2 SECT:105 OBJ:116 RAND:Y

39. ANS:51 TYPE:S DIFF:2 SECT:106 OBJ:119 RAND:Y

40. ANS:-19 TYPE:S DIFF:3 SECT:106 OBJ:119 RAND:Y

41. ANS:3y - 6 TYPE:S DIFF:2 SECT:106 OBJ:120 RAND:Y

42. TYPE:S DIFF:3 SECT:106 OBJ:120 RAND:Y

ANSWER:
    $\frac{12}{x^2} = 14$

43. ANS:4 TYPE:S DIFF:2 SECT:106 OBJ:121 RAND:Y

44. ANS:13 + 2x TYPE:S DIFF:2 SECT:107 OBJ:123 RAND:Y

45. ANS:15 - 6x TYPE:S DIFF:2 SECT:107 OBJ:123 RAND:Y

46. ANS:3y - 5 TYPE:S DIFF:2 SECT:107 OBJ:123 RAND:Y

47. TYPE:S DIFF:3 SECT:107 OBJ:123 RAND:Y

ANSWER:
    -0.4x + 1.6

48. TYPE:S DIFF:2 SECT:107 OBJ:124 RAND:Y

ANSWER:
    28,800 pounds

49. TYPE:S DIFF:2 SECT:107 OBJ:122 RAND:Y

ANSWER:
     commutative property of addition

50. TYPE:S DIFF:1 SECT:107 OBJ:122 RAND:Y

ANSWER:
     associative property of multiplication

51. ANS:**b** TYPE:**M** DIFF:1 SECT:101 OBJ:101 RAND:**Y**

52. ANS:**c** TYPE:**M** DIFF:2 SECT:101 OBJ:101 RAND:**Y**

53. ANS:**a** TYPE:**M** DIFF:2 SECT:101 OBJ:102 RAND:**Y**

54. ANS:**b** TYPE:**M** DIFF:1 SECT:101 OBJ:102 RAND:**Y**

55. ANS:**d** TYPE:**M** DIFF:3 SECT:101 OBJ:104 RAND:**Y**

56. ANS:**e** TYPE:**M** DIFF:2 SECT:101 OBJ:102 RAND:**Y**

57. ANS:**a** TYPE:**M** DIFF:2 SECT:101 OBJ:104 RAND:**Y**

58. ANS:**c** TYPE:**M** DIFF:2 SECT:101 OBJ:104 RAND:**Y**

59. ANS:**e** TYPE:**M** DIFF:1 SECT:101 OBJ:103 RAND:**Y**

60. ANS:**d** TYPE:**M** DIFF:2 SECT:102 OBJ:105 RAND:**Y**

61. ANS:**c** TYPE:**M** DIFF:2 SECT:102 OBJ:106 RAND:**Y**

62. ANS:**d** TYPE:**M** DIFF:1 SECT:102 OBJ:105 RAND:**Y**

63. ANS:**a** TYPE:**M** DIFF:1 SECT:102 OBJ:107 RAND:**Y**

64. ANS:**d** TYPE:**M** DIFF:2 SECT:102 OBJ:107 RAND:**Y**

23

65. ANS:a TYPE:M DIFF:3 SECT:102 OBJ:107 RAND:Y

66. ANS:b TYPE:M DIFF:1 SECT:103 OBJ:110 RAND:Y

67. ANS:b TYPE:M DIFF:1 SECT:103 OBJ:110 RAND:Y

68. ANS:c TYPE:M DIFF:2 SECT:103 OBJ:111 RAND:Y

69. ANS:a TYPE:M DIFF:2 SECT:103 OBJ:111 RAND:Y

70. ANS:c TYPE:M DIFF:1 SECT:103 OBJ:108 GRAPH FORMAT:G
    QUESTION GRAPH:3 RAND:Y

71. ANS:c TYPE:M DIFF:1 SECT:103 OBJ:109 RAND:Y

72. ANS:d TYPE:M DIFF:1 SECT:104 OBJ:113 RAND:Y

73. ANS:e TYPE:M DIFF:2 SECT:104 OBJ:112 RAND:Y

74. ANS:b TYPE:M DIFF:3 SECT:104 OBJ:114 RAND:Y

75. ANS:c TYPE:M DIFF:3 SECT:104 OBJ:114 RAND:Y

76. ANS:d TYPE:M DIFF:2 SECT:104 OBJ:114 RAND:Y

77. ANS:a TYPE:M DIFF:2 SECT:104 OBJ:115 RAND:Y

78. ANS:e TYPE:M DIFF:3 SECT:104 OBJ:114 RAND:Y

79. ANS:c TYPE:M DIFF:2 SECT:104 OBJ:114 RAND:Y

80. ANS:b TYPE:M DIFF:1 SECT:104 OBJ:112 RAND:Y

81. ANS:e TYPE:M DIFF:1 SECT:105 OBJ:116 RAND:Y

82. ANS:b TYPE:M DIFF:2 SECT:105 OBJ:116 RAND:Y

83. ANS:c TYPE:M DIFF:1 SECT:105 OBJ:118 RAND:Y

84. ANS:b TYPE:M DIFF:2 SECT:105 OBJ:116 RAND:Y

85. ANS:d TYPE:M DIFF:3 SECT:105 OBJ:116 RAND:Y

86. ANS:c TYPE:M DIFF:2 SECT:105 OBJ:117 RAND:Y

87. ANS:d TYPE:M DIFF:3 SECT:105 OBJ:116 RAND:Y

88. ANS:b TYPE:M DIFF:2 SECT:105 OBJ:116 RAND:Y

89. ANS:c TYPE:M DIFF:2 SECT:106 OBJ:119 RAND:Y

90. ANS:a TYPE:M DIFF:2 SECT:106 OBJ:119 RAND:Y

91. ANS:b TYPE:M DIFF:2 SECT:106 OBJ:120 RAND:Y

92. ANS:d TYPE:M DIFF:3 SECT:106 OBJ:120 RAND:Y

93. ANS:c TYPE:M DIFF:2 SECT:106 OBJ:121 RAND:Y

94. ANS:b TYPE:M DIFF:2 SECT:107 OBJ:123 RAND:Y

95. ANS:d TYPE:M DIFF:2 SECT:107 OBJ:123 RAND:Y

96. ANS:e TYPE:M DIFF:2 SECT:107 OBJ:123 RAND:Y

97. ANS:b TYPE:M DIFF:3 SECT:107 OBJ:123 RAND:Y

98. ANS:d TYPE:M DIFF:2 SECT:107 OBJ:124 RAND:Y

99. ANS:b TYPE:M DIFF:2 SECT:107 OBJ:122 RAND:Y

100. ANS:c TYPE:M DIFF:2 SECT:107 OBJ:122 RAND:Y

CHAPTER 2: LINEAR EQUATIONS AND INEQUALITIES

SHORT ANSWER

1. Find the coefficient of a^2 in the expression:

$$5a^4 + 2a^3 - 3a^2 + 6$$

2. Simplify by combining like terms:

$$6 + y - 3y + 11$$

3. Simplify by combining like terms:

$$5 - 2(xy - 9) + 5(yz - xy) + 3xy$$

4. Simplify by combining like terms:

$$12x - 3(2 - 5x^2) + 4(x - 9) - 4x^2$$

5. Simplify:

$$\frac{2}{3}(6x - 5) - \frac{5}{8}\left[\frac{16}{15} - x\right]$$

6. Solve:

$$x - 2 = -31$$

7. Solve:

$$6x + 1 = 5x - 9$$

8. Solve:

$$\frac{2}{3}x = -12$$

9. Solve:

$$\frac{x}{6.8} = 0.34$$

10. Solve:

$$y - \frac{1}{5}y = 1\frac{1}{2} - 4\frac{3}{4}$$

11. Solve:

$$5 - 10y = 7$$

12. Solve:

$$3x + 4 = 9x - 1$$

13. Solve:

$$5x + 3(2 - 9x) = 4(1 - 5x)$$

14. Solve:

$$19 - 3(5 - w) = 4(2w - 3) - (w - 2)$$

15. Solve:

$$4 - (2 + 3a) = 5(2a - 1)$$

16. Solve:

$$11 - 2(x - 9) = 3x + 9(x - 2)$$

17. Solve:

$$2x + 5(x - 3) = 4x - 11$$

18. Convert the following phrase into an algebraic expression, using x for the variable:

   "Fifteen less than two-thirds of a number."

19. Convert the following phrase into an algebraic expression, using x for the variable:

   "The reciprocal of twice a number."

20. The sum of twice a number and 5.3 is -9.26. Find the number.

21. Twelve less than twenty percent of a number is 43. Find the number.

22. Twice the difference of a number and $\frac{1}{2}$ is $5\frac{1}{3}$. Find the number.

23. Anthony is paid $550 a week plus a commission of 8% on sales. Find the sales in dollars, needed to give him a weekly total of $800.

24. The Computer Outlet is selling a floor model computer system for 30% off. If the sale price is $1,386, what was the original price?

25. The sum of three consecutive even integers is -72. Find the three integers.

26. Rhonda is planning to cut a fourteen-foot board into two pieces. The length of the longer piece must be twice the length of the shorter piece. Find the lengths of the two pieces. Express your answer as mixed numbers.

29

ESSAY

27. Matt is 10 years older than his brother. Three years ago, Matt was three times as old as his brother. How old is Matt now?

28. Sharon is 3 years younger than her sister. Four years ago, Sharon was half as old as her sister. How old is Sharon now?

29. Tanya has $2.95 in nickels and dimes. If she has five more nickels than dimes, how many coins of each type does she have?

30. One insulin solution contains 5% zinc crystals. Another insulin solution contains 9% zinc crystals. How many liters of each solution should be used to make a 300-liter solution that contains 8% zinc crystals?

31. The Nut House is planning to sell a 30-ounce box of nuts containing almonds and cashews. If the almonds cost 30 cents per ounce, and the cashews cost 90 cents per ounce, and the box of nuts is to cost $15, how many ounces of each type of nut should one box contain?

SHORT ANSWER

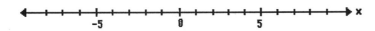

32. On the above number line, graph x < -2

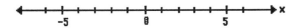

33. On the above number line, graph x $\geq$ -3

34. Solve, and graph your solution on a number line:

$$x + 5 \geq 7$$

35. Solve, and graph your solution on a number line:

$$5 + 4x < 3x + 2$$

36. Solve, and graph your solution on a number line:

$$-2 < x + 2 \leq 5$$

37. Solve, and graph your solution on a number line:

$$-3t \geq 12$$

38. Solve, and graph your solution on a number line:

$$-\frac{3}{5}x < \frac{9}{10}$$

30

39. Solve, and graph your solution on a number line:

$$4x + 9 < 5x - 3 + 2x$$

40. Solve, and graph your solution on a number line:

$$5 < 2x - 3 \leq 9$$

41. Solve, and graph your solution on a number line:

$$-3 < 5 - 4x \leq 9$$

42. Solve the following inequality:

"The difference of five times a number and two is greater than or equal to negative four, but less than three."

43. Rick and James leave work at the same time and walk in opposite directions. If Rick walks at a rate of 3 mph and James walks at a rate of 2 mph, how long will it take for them to be 2 miles apart? (answer in minutes)

44. Kit is planning to invest $10,000, part in an investment paying 7% and the rest in an investment paying 12%. How much should he invest at each rate to realize an $1,125 yearly interest payment?

45. The measure of the first angle in a triangle is three times the measure of the second angle and the measure of the third angle is two degrees less than the measure of the first angle. Find the measure of each angle.

46. A rectangular field has dimensions 90 feet by 30 feet. If fencing costs $8 per foot, how much will it cost to enclose the field with a fence?

47. Solve $I = Prt$ for P

48. Solve $y = ab + c$ for b

49. Solve $y = \dfrac{4x - 5}{3}$ for x

50. Solve $P = 31 - 5t$ for t

MULTIPLE CHOICE

51. Find the coefficient of b^3 in the expression:

$$4b^5 + 3b^4 - 9b^3 + b^2 - 11$$

a. 4
b. 9
c. 1
d. 0
e. none of these

52. Simplify by combining like terms:

$$9 + x - 5x + 8$$

a. $17 - 5x$
b. $17 - 4x$
c. $13x$
d. $1 - 4x$
e. none of these

53. Simplify by combining like terms:

$$3wx - 4(xy - 5) + 8(wx + 3xy) - 42$$

a. $11wx + 20xy - 22$
b. $11wx - xy - 47$
c. $9wx^2 y$
d. $11wx - xy - 22$
e. none of these

54. Simplify by combining like terms:

$$25t - 9(3 - 4t^2) + 3(2t - 11) - 6t^2$$

a. $-42t^2 + 31t - 60$
b. $30t^2 + 31t - 60$
c. $-10t^2 + 31t - 38$
d. $-30t^2 - 31t - 38$
e. none of these

55. Simplify:

$$\frac{5}{2}\left(8x - \frac{9}{10}\right) - \frac{3}{10}\left(\frac{2}{5} - 5x\right)$$

a. $\frac{55x}{12} - \frac{17}{30}$

b. $\frac{43x}{2} - \frac{237}{100}$

c. $15x - \frac{51}{50}$

d. $25x - \frac{51}{50}$

e. none of these

56. Solve:

$$x - 5 = -46$$

a. -51

b. $\frac{46}{5}$

c. -41

d. 230

e. none of these

57. Solve:

$$4x + 3 = 3x - 11$$

a. -8

b. -14

c. -2

d. $-\frac{8}{7}$

e. none of these

58. Solve:

$$\frac{5}{6}x = -30$$

a. -25
b. -36
c. 25
d. 36

59. Solve:

$$\frac{y}{2.8} = 0.07$$

a. 0.196

b. $\frac{1}{4}$

c. $\frac{1}{40}$

d. 19.6

e. none of these

60. Solve:

$$x - \frac{3}{8}x = 2\frac{1}{5} - 5\frac{3}{4}$$

a. $-\frac{12}{25}$

b. $-\frac{71}{5}$

c. $-\frac{159}{5}$

d. $-\frac{142}{25}$

e. none of these

61. Solve:

$$3 - 8y = 5$$

a. -4

b. $-\dfrac{1}{4}$

c. -1

d. -10

e. none of these

62. Solve:

$$2x + 5 = 9x - 3$$

a. $\dfrac{8}{7}$

b. $\dfrac{7}{8}$

c. $\dfrac{2}{7}$

d. $\dfrac{2}{11}$

e. none of these

63. Solve:

$$4y + 8(3 - 2y) = 5(4 - 2y)$$

a. 0

b. $1\dfrac{1}{2}$

c. $2\dfrac{2}{3}$

d. $3\dfrac{1}{12}$

e. none of these

35

64. Solve:

$$15 - 5(4 - x) = 3(2x + 1) - (2x - 9)$$

a. 17

b. 2

c. $\frac{1}{3}$

d. 27

e. none of these

65. Solve:

$$5 - (11 + 9t) = 4(8t - 1)$$

a. $-\frac{2}{23}$

b. $\frac{2}{23}$

c. $-\frac{2}{41}$

d. $\frac{2}{41}$

e. none of these

66. Solve:

$$15 - 9(y - 3) = 4y + 3(y - 11)$$

a. $\frac{23}{16}$

b. 15

c. 8

d. $\frac{75}{16}$

e. none of these

67. Solve:

$$4x + 9(x - 2) = 10x - 8$$

   a. -2

   b. $\dfrac{-26}{3}$

   c. $\dfrac{10}{3}$

   d. $-\dfrac{10}{3}$

   e. none of these

68. Convert the following phrase into an algebraic expression, using x for the variable:

   "Eight less than twice a number."

   a. 2(x - 8)
   b. 2(8 - x)
   c. 2x - 8
   d. 8 - 2x
   e. none of these

69. Convert the following phrase into an algebraic expression, using x for the variable:

   "The reciprocal of the sum of a number and 4."

   a. $\dfrac{1}{x} + 4$

   b. $\dfrac{1}{4x}$

   c. $\dfrac{1}{x + 4}$

   d. $\dfrac{1}{4} + x$

   e. none of these

70. The sum of three times a number and 8.2 is -22.46. Find the number.

   a. -14.26
   b. -30.66
   c. -15.33
   d. -11.26
   e. none of these

71. Six more than 30% of a number is 93. Find the number.

   a. 29
   b. 33
   c. 290
   d. 330
   e. none of these

72. Twice the sum of a number and $\frac{3}{4}$ is $8\frac{1}{2}$. Find the number.

   a. $\frac{7}{2}$

   b. $\frac{31}{8}$

   c. $\frac{17}{3}$

   d. $\frac{17}{6}$

   e. none of these

73. The larger of two numbers is 5.8 more than the smaller.
   If the larger is negative two thirds times the smaller,
   find the larger number.

   a. -8.7

   b. 2.9

   c. $-\frac{87}{25}$

   d. $\frac{58}{25}$

   e. none of these

74. Rosa bought a dress on sale for 40% off the original price. If she
   paid $51, what was the original price?

   a. $127.50
   b. $71.40
   c. $85.00
   d. $81.60
   e. none of these

75. The sum of three consecutive odd integers is -39. Which of the following equations could be used to find the smallest of the integers?

    a. x + 2x + 3x = -39
    b. x +(x + 1) + (x + 2) = -39
    c. x + (x + 3) + (x + 6) = -39
    d. x + (x + 2) + (x + 4) = -39
    e. none of these

76. Shana is planning to cut a 26 foot board into two pieces. The length of the longer piece must be five feet less twice the length of the shorter piece. Find the length of the longer piece.

    a. 21 feet

    b. $18\frac{1}{3}$ feet

    c. $15\frac{2}{3}$ feet

    d. $20\frac{2}{3}$ feet

    e. none of these

77. Rick is five years older than his brother. Four years ago, Rick was twice as old as his brother. How old is Rick now?

    a. 9
    b. 10
    c. 12
    d. 14
    e. none of these

78. Kara is four years younger than her sister. Two years from now, Kara will be nine tenths as old as her sister. How old is Kara now?

    a. 34
    b. 38
    c. 54
    d. 58
    e. none of these

79. Sylvia has $2.40 in nickels and dimes. If she has three more dimes than nickels, how many dimes does she have?

    a. 14
    b. 17
    c. 15
    d. 18
    e. none of these

80. A chemist has one solution containing a 10% concentration of acid
    and a second solution containing a 15% concentration of acid. How
    many milliliters of each solution should be used to make a 200
    milliliter solution containing a 12% concentration of acid?

    a. 140 ml of the 10% and 60 ml of the 15%
    b. 130 ml of the 10% and 70 ml of the 15%
    c. 120 ml of the 10% and 80 ml of the 15%
    d. 110 ml of the 10% and 90 ml of the 15%
    e. none of these

81. Ye Olde Tea House is planning to sell a 32 ounce tin of tea
    containing orange pekoe and green mint. If the orange pekoe costs
    40 cents per ounce and the green mint costs 50 cents per ounce, and
    the tin of tea is to cost $13, how many ounces of orange pekoe
    should one tin contain?

    a. 20
    b. 24
    c. 28
    d. 30
    e. none of these

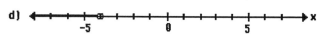

e) none of these

82. Which of the above graphs is a correct graph of x < -4?

e) none of these

83. Which of the above is a graph of -2 ≤ x < 5?

40

84. Solve:

$$x + 3 \geq -4$$

a. $x \leq -7$
b. $x \leq -1$
c. $x \geq -7$
d. $x \geq 1$
e. none of these

85. Solve:

$$9 + 2x < x + 3$$

a. $x < -2$
b. $x < 4$
c. $x < 12$
d. $x < 6$
e. none of these

86. Solve:

$$-5 < y + 5 \leq 8$$

a. $0 < y \leq 3$
b. $-1 < y \leq 3$
c. $-10 < y \leq 3$
d. $0 < y < 13$
e. none of these

87. Solve:

$$-6w \geq 18$$

a. $w \geq -3$
b. $w \geq 24$
c. $w \leq -3$
d. $w \leq 24$
e. none of these

88. Solve:

$$-\frac{3}{2}x < 6$$

a. $x > -4$
b. $x > -9$
c. $x < -4$
d. $x < -9$
e. none of these

41

89. Solve:

$$5t + 8 \leq 6t - 1 + 8t$$

   a. $t \leq 1$

   b. $t \geq 1$

   c. $t \leq -\dfrac{7}{9}$

   d. $t \geq -\dfrac{7}{9}$

   e. none of these

90. Solve:

$$3 < 4x - 5 \leq 7$$

   a. $-\dfrac{1}{2} < x \leq \dfrac{1}{2}$

   b. $4 < x \leq 8$

   c. $2 < x \leq 12$

   d. $8 < x \leq 12$

   e. none of these

91. Solve:

$$-9 \leq 5 - 2x < 3$$

   a. $1 < x \leq 7$
   b. $7 \leq x < 1$
   c. $2 \leq x < 4$
   d. $-12 \leq x < 0$
   e. none of these

92. Solve the following inequality:

   "The sum of three times a number and one is greater than or equal to negative eight, but less than ten."

   a. $-\dfrac{7}{3} \leq x < \dfrac{11}{3}$

   b. $-\dfrac{11}{3} \leq x < \dfrac{7}{3}$

   c. $-3 \leq x < 3$

   d. $-12 \leq x < 6$

   e. none of these

42

93. The volume of a cylinder is given by $V = \pi r^2 h$. How long must you make a cylindrical container whose radius is 3 inches if you want the volume to be $720\,\pi$ cubic inches?

    a. 120 inches
    b. $240\,\pi$ inches
    c. 80 inches
    d. $6{,}480\,\pi$ inches
    e. none of these

94. Two planes, flying in opposite directions, pass each other. One is flying at 240 mph and the other at 300 mph. How long will it take for them to be 108 miles apart?

    a. 20 minutes
    b. 2 minutes
    c. 15 minutes
    d. 12 minutes
    e. none of these

95. Steve is planning to invest $20,000, part at 12% and the other part at 15%, for one year. If he wants the total interest for the year to be $2,730, how much should he invest at 15%?

    a. $8,000
    b. $12,000
    c. $9,000
    d. $11,000
    e. none of these

96. A company that makes coffee tables has a weekly cost C of $C = 49{,}110 + 50x$, where x is the number of coffee tables made and sold in a week. The weekly revenue R is given by $R = 80x$. Find the break-even level for the company.

    a. 30 tables
    b. 983 tables
    c. 1,637 tables
    d. 48,980 tables
    e. none of these

97. Solve:

    $$V = lwh \text{ for } w$$

    a. $w = V - lh$
    b. $w = \dfrac{lh}{V}$
    c. $w = \dfrac{V}{lh}$
    d. $w = \dfrac{V - l}{h}$
    e. none of these

98. Solve:

$$R = mt + a \quad \text{for } t$$

a. $t = \dfrac{R}{ma}$

b. $t = \dfrac{R}{m + a}$

c. $t = \dfrac{R - m}{a}$

d. $t = \dfrac{R - a}{m}$

e. none of these

99. Solve:

$$M = \dfrac{5w - T}{2} \quad \text{for } w$$

a. $w = \dfrac{2M + T}{5}$

b. $w = \dfrac{2M}{5 - T}$

c. $w = \dfrac{2M}{5T}$

d. $w = \dfrac{M}{5} + 2T$

e. none of these

100. Solve:

$$y = 3w - 9x \quad \text{for } x$$

a. $x = \dfrac{y}{3w - 9}$

b. $x = \dfrac{y - 3w}{9}$

c. $x = \dfrac{y + 9}{3w}$

d. $x = y - 3w + 9$

e. none of these

1. ANS:-3 TYPE:S DIFF:1 SECT:201 OBJ:201 RAND:Y

2. ANS:17 - 2y TYPE:S DIFF:1 SECT:201 OBJ:202 RAND:Y

3. TYPE:S DIFF:2 SECT:201 OBJ:202 RAND:Y

ANSWER:
      23 + 5yz - 4xy

4. TYPE:S DIFF:2 SECT:201 OBJ:202 RAND:Y

ANSWER:
      $11x^2$ + 16x - 42

5. TYPE:S DIFF:3 SECT:201 OBJ:202 RAND:Y

ANSWER:
      $\frac{37}{8}x$ - 4

6. ANS:-29 TYPE:S DIFF:1 SECT:202 OBJ:203 RAND:Y

7. ANS:-10 TYPE:S DIFF:1 SECT:202 OBJ:203 RAND:Y

8. ANS:-18 TYPE:S DIFF:1 SECT:203 OBJ:204 RAND:Y

9. ANS:2.312 TYPE:S DIFF:2 SECT:203 OBJ:204 RAND:Y

10. TYPE:S DIFF:3 SECT:203 OBJ:204 RAND:Y

ANSWER:
      $-\frac{65}{16}$ or $-4\frac{1}{16}$ or -4.0625

11. TYPE:S DIFF:1 SECT:204 OBJ:205 RAND:Y

ANSWER:
      $-\frac{1}{5}$

12. TYPE:S DIFF:1 SECT:204 OBJ:205 RAND:Y

ANSWER:
$$\frac{5}{6}$$

13. ANS:1 TYPE:S DIFF:2 SECT:204 OBJ:205 RAND:Y

14. TYPE:S DIFF:3 SECT:204 OBJ:205 RAND:Y

ANSWER:
$$\frac{7}{2} \text{ or } 3\frac{1}{2}$$

15. TYPE:S DIFF:2 SECT:204 OBJ:205 RAND:Y

ANSWER:
$$\frac{7}{13}$$

16. TYPE:S DIFF:3 SECT:204 OBJ:205 RAND:Y

ANSWER:
$$\frac{47}{14}$$

17. TYPE:S DIFF:2 SECT:204 OBJ:205 RAND:Y

ANSWER:
$$\frac{4}{3}$$

18. TYPE:S DIFF:2 SECT:205 OBJ:206 RAND:Y

ANSWER:
$$\frac{2}{3}x - 15$$

19. TYPE:S DIFF:2 SECT:205 OBJ:206 RAND:Y

ANSWER:
$$\frac{1}{2x}$$

20. ANS:-7.28 TYPE:S DIFF:2 SECT:205 OBJ:207 RAND:Y

21. ANS:275   TYPE:S   DIFF:2   SECT:205   OBJ:207   RAND:Y

22. TYPE:S   DIFF:2   SECT:205   OBJ:207   RAND:Y

ANSWER:
$\frac{19}{6}$ or $3\frac{1}{6}$

23. ANS:$3,125   TYPE:S   DIFF:2   SECT:206   OBJ:208   RAND:Y

24. ANS:$1,980   TYPE:S   DIFF:2   SECT:206   OBJ:208   RAND:Y

25. TYPE:S   DIFF:2   SECT:206   OBJ:208   RAND:Y

ANSWER:
     -26, -24, -22

26. TYPE:S   DIFF:2   SECT:206   OBJ:208   RAND:Y

ANSWER:
     $4\frac{2}{3}$ feet, $9\frac{1}{3}$ feet

27. ANS:18   TYPE:E   DIFF:2   SECT:206   OBJ:209   RAND:Y

28. ANS:7   TYPE:E   DIFF:2   SECT:206   OBJ:209   RAND:Y

29. TYPE:E   DIFF:2   SECT:206   OBJ:210   RAND:Y

ANSWER:
     23 nickels and 18 dimes

30. TYPE:E   DIFF:2   SECT:206   OBJ:211   RAND:Y

ANSWER:
     75 liters of the 5% solution; 225 liters of the 9% solution

31. TYPE:E   DIFF:2   SECT:206   OBJ:211   RAND:Y

ANSWER:
     20 ounces of almonds, 10 ounces of cashews.

32. TYPE:**S** DIFF:**1** SECT:**207** OBJ:**212** GRAPH FORMAT:**G**
QUESTION GRAPH:**1** ANSWER GRAPH:**2** RAND:**Y**

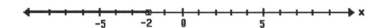

33. TYPE:**S** DIFF:**1** SECT:**207** OBJ:**212** GRAPH FORMAT:**G**
QUESTION GRAPH:**3** ANSWER GRAPH:**4** RAND:**Y**

34. TYPE:**S** DIFF:**1** SECT:**207** OBJ:**213** ANSWER GRAPH:**5** RAND:**Y**

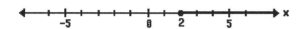

35. ANS:**x > −3** TYPE:**S** DIFF:**2** SECT:**207** OBJ:**213** ANSWER GRAPH:**6**
RAND:**Y**

36. TYPE:**S** DIFF:**2** SECT:**207** OBJ:**213** ANSWER GRAPH:**7** RAND:**Y**

ANSWER:
   $-4 < x \le 3$

37. TYPE:**S** DIFF:**1** SECT:**208** OBJ:**214** ANSWER GRAPH:**8** RAND:**Y**

ANSWER:
   $t \le -4$

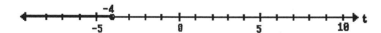

48

38. TYPE:S DIFF:2 SECT:208 OBJ:214 ANSWER GRAPH:9 RAND:Y

ANSWER:
x > -3/2 or x > -1 1/2

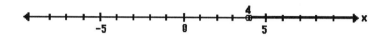

39. ANS:**x > 4** TYPE:S DIFF:2 SECT:208 OBJ:215 ANSWER GRAPH:10
RAND:**Y**

40. TYPE:S DIFF:2 SECT:208 OBJ:215 ANSWER GRAPH:11 RAND:Y

ANSWER:
4 < x ≤ 6

41. TYPE:S DIFF:3 SECT:208 OBJ:215 ANSWER GRAPH:12 RAND:Y

ANSWER:
-1 ≤ x < 2

42. TYPE:S DIFF:3 SECT:208 OBJ:216 RAND:Y

ANSWER:
$-\frac{2}{5} \le x < 1$

43. TYPE:S DIFF:2 SECT:209 OBJ:217 RAND:Y

ANSWER:
24 minutes

49

44. TYPE:S DIFF:3 SECT:209 OBJ:217 RAND:Y

ANSWER:
    $1,500 at 7%, $8,500 at 12%

45. TYPE:S DIFF:2 SECT:209 OBJ:217 RAND:Y

ANSWER:
    78°, 26°, 76°

46. ANS:$1,920 TYPE:S DIFF:2 SECT:209 OBJ:217 RAND:Y

47. TYPE:S DIFF:1 SECT:209 OBJ:218 RAND:Y

ANSWER:
    $P = \dfrac{I}{rt}$

48. TYPE:S DIFF:2 SECT:209 OBJ:218 RAND:Y

ANSWER:
    $b = \dfrac{y-c}{a}$

49. TYPE:S DIFF:2 SECT:209 OBJ:218 RAND:Y

ANSWER:
    $x = \dfrac{3y + 5}{4}$

50. TYPE:S DIFF:2 SECT:209 OBJ:218 RAND:Y

ANSWER:
    $t = \dfrac{31 - P}{5}$

51. ANS:e TYPE:M DIFF:1 SECT:201 OBJ:201 RAND:Y

52. ANS:b TYPE:M DIFF:1 SECT:201 OBJ:202 RAND:Y

53. ANS:a TYPE:M DIFF:2 SECT:201 OBJ:202 RAND:Y

54. ANS:b TYPE:M DIFF:2 SECT:201 OBJ:202 RAND:Y

55. ANS:b TYPE:M DIFF:3 SECT:201 OBJ:202 RAND:Y

56. ANS:c TYPE:M DIFF:1 SECT:202 OBJ:203 RAND:Y

57. ANS:b TYPE:M DIFF:1 SECT:202 OBJ:203 RAND:Y

58. ANS:b TYPE:M DIFF:1 SECT:203 OBJ:204 RAND:Y

59. ANS:a TYPE:M DIFF:2 SECT:203 OBJ:204 RAND:Y

60. ANS:d TYPE:M DIFF:3 SECT:203 OBJ:204 RAND:Y

61. ANS:b TYPE:M DIFF:1 SECT:204 OBJ:205 RAND:Y

62. ANS:a TYPE:M DIFF:1 SECT:204 OBJ:205 RAND:Y

63. ANS:e TYPE:M DIFF:2 SECT:204 OBJ:205 RAND:Y

64. ANS:a TYPE:M DIFF:3 SECT:204 OBJ:205 RAND:Y

65. ANS:c TYPE:M DIFF:2 SECT:204 OBJ:205 RAND:Y

66. ANS:d TYPE:M DIFF:3 SECT:204 OBJ:205 RAND:Y

67. ANS:c TYPE:M DIFF:2 SECT:204 OBJ:205 RAND:Y

68. ANS:c TYPE:M DIFF:2 SECT:205 OBJ:206 RAND:Y

69. ANS:c TYPE:M DIFF:2 SECT:205 OBJ:206 RAND:Y

70. ANS:e TYPE:M DIFF:2 SECT:205 OBJ:207 RAND:Y

71. ANS:c TYPE:M DIFF:2 SECT:205 OBJ:207 RAND:Y

72. ANS:a TYPE:M DIFF:2 SECT:205 OBJ:207 RAND:Y

73. ANS:d TYPE:M DIFF:3 SECT:206 OBJ:208 RAND:Y

74. ANS:c TYPE:M DIFF:2 SECT:206 OBJ:208 RAND:Y

75. ANS:d TYPE:M DIFF:2 SECT:206 OBJ:208 RAND:Y

76. ANS:c TYPE:M DIFF:2 SECT:206 OBJ:208 RAND:Y

77. ANS:d TYPE:M DIFF:2 SECT:206 OBJ:209 RAND:Y

78. ANS:a TYPE:M DIFF:2 SECT:206 OBJ:209 RAND:Y

79. ANS:b TYPE:M DIFF:2 SECT:206 OBJ:210 RAND:Y

80. ANS:c TYPE:M DIFF:2 SECT:206 OBJ:211 RAND:Y

81. ANS:d TYPE:M DIFF:2 SECT:206 OBJ:211 RAND:Y

82. ANS:d TYPE:M DIFF:1 SECT:207 OBJ:212 GRAPH FORMAT:G
    QUESTION GRAPH:13 RAND:Y

83. ANS:a TYPE:M DIFF:2 SECT:207 OBJ:212 GRAPH FORMAT:G
    QUESTION GRAPH:14 RAND:Y

84. ANS:c TYPE:M DIFF:1 SECT:207 OBJ:213 RAND:Y

85. ANS:e TYPE:M DIFF:2 SECT:207 OBJ:213 RAND:Y

86. ANS:c TYPE:M DIFF:2 SECT:207 OBJ:213 RAND:Y

87. ANS:c TYPE:M DIFF:1 SECT:208 OBJ:214 RAND:Y

88. ANS:a TYPE:M DIFF:2 SECT:208 OBJ:214 RAND:Y

89. ANS:b TYPE:M DIFF:2 SECT:208 OBJ:215 RAND:Y

90. ANS:e TYPE:M DIFF:2 SECT:208 OBJ:215 RAND:Y

91. ANS:a   TYPE:M   DIFF:3   SECT:208   OBJ:215   RAND:Y

92. ANS:c   TYPE:M   DIFF:3   SECT:208   OBJ:216   RAND:Y

93. ANS:c   TYPE:M   DIFF:1   SECT:209   OBJ:217   RAND:Y

94. ANS:d   TYPE:M   DIFF:2   SECT:209   OBJ:217   RAND:Y

95. ANS:d   TYPE:M   DIFF:2   SECT:209   OBJ:217   RAND:Y

96. ANS:c   TYPE:M   DIFF:2   SECT:209   OBJ:217   RAND:Y

97. ANS:c   TYPE:M   DIFF:1   SECT:209   OBJ:218   RAND:Y

98. ANS:d   TYPE:M   DIFF:2   SECT:209   OBJ:218   RAND:Y

99. ANS:a   TYPE:M   DIFF:2   SECT:209   OBJ:218   RAND:Y

100. ANS:e   TYPE:M   DIFF:2   SECT:209   OBJ:218   RAND:Y

CHAPTER 3:   EXPONENTS AND POLYNOMIALS

SHORT ANSWER

1. Find the value of $(-2)^4$

2. Find the value of -4^2

3. Simplify:

   $x^4 \ x^{10}$

4. Simplify:

   $b^5 \cdot b \cdot b^9$

5. Simplify:

   $(x^5)^4$

6. Simplify:

   $(4w^2)^3$

7. Simplify:

   $y^5 \ (y^2)^{10}$

8. Simplify:

   $(x^6)^2 \ x^{10}$

9. Simplify:

   $(2x^2)^3 \ (5x^4)^2$

10. Find the value of 4^0

11. Simplify (assume that the variables are nonzero):

    $(2x + 3y)^0$

12. Write the expression without negative exponents:

    x^{-3}

13. Write the expression without negative exponents:

    $(2x)^{-5}$

14. Simplify and write your answer without negative exponents:

    $$\frac{3^{20}}{3^{18}}$$

15. Simplify and write your answer without negative exponents:

$$\frac{45y^6}{15y^9}$$

16. Simplify and write your answer without negative exponents:

$$\left(\frac{2x}{z^2}\right)^{-4}$$

17. Simplify and write your answer without negative exponents:

$$\frac{5x^{-2}}{20x^{-8}}$$

18. Simplify and write your answer without negative exponents:

$$\frac{(x^{-2}w^3)^{-3}}{(xw^2)^4}$$

19. Write in scientific notation:

0.0036

20. Write in scientific notation:

295002

21. Multiply $-\frac{3}{5}(x^2y^4)^3$ by $(10xy^2)^2$

22. Simplify:

$$(5x^3y^2)(-3x^5y)$$

23. Divide $5a^3b^2$ by a^2b^2

24. Simplify (answer with positive exponents):

$$\frac{(-4x^2y^3)^2}{(2x^5y)(6x^2y^8)}$$

25. Simplify (answer with positive exponents):

$$\frac{12x^2y^{15}}{(2x^3y^2)^4}$$

26. Determine if the following polynomial is a monomial, binomial, trinomial, or none of these:

$$2y^3 + 6y - 1$$

57

27. Determine if the following polynomial is a monomial, binomial, trinomial, or none of these:

$$4xyz$$

28. Find the degree of $2a^5 - 6a^8 + 3a^2 - 2$

29. Find the degree of $3x^2 - 5x^4 + 11x^5 + 20$

30. Simplify:

$$-(12x^2yz^4 - z^5) - (2x^2yz^4 + 3x^2)$$

31. Simplify:

$$5a^2b - 2(3ab^2 - 5) + 11$$

32. Add the polynomials:

$$(x^4 - 3x^2 + 2x - 5) + (3x^4 + x^3 - 5x + 3)$$

33. Subtract the first polynomial from the second:

$$6t^3 + 5t^2 - 9, \quad 4t^3 - 3t^2 + 11t$$

34. Subtract the first polynomial from the second:

$$\frac{3}{4}z^4 - \frac{2}{3}z^2 + \frac{5}{6}, \quad \frac{1}{4}z^3 - \frac{1}{6}z^2 + \frac{1}{2}z - \frac{1}{8}$$

35. Simplify (write your answer in descending order of the exponents):

$$(5r^3 - 2r + 3) - (4r + 3r^2 - 2) + (11 - 2r^3 + 9r^2)$$

36. Simplify (write your answer in descending order of the exponents):

$$-3x^5 + 2x^3 - [-2x^5 - (3x^3 - 14x^5)]$$

37. Multiply:

$$x^4(x^3 - 3x^2 + 9x - 3)$$

38. Multiply:

$$-\frac{2}{5}y^2 \left[\frac{15}{8}y^3 - 10y^2 + \frac{3}{2}\right]$$

39. Multiply:

$$-5w^2t^3(-3w^4t^5 + 2w^3t^2 + 3w - 11t)$$

40. Multiply:

$$(x + 3)(x - 5)$$

58

41. Multiply:

$$(y - 6)(y - 3)$$

42. Multiply:

$$(2y - 3)(5y + 2)$$

43. Multiply:

$$(3n - 7y)(5n + y)$$

44. Multiply:

$$(5t + 4)(2t^2 - 11t + 9)$$

45. Find the product:

$$(4a + b)^2$$

46. Find the product:

$$\left(\frac{2}{3}x - \frac{3}{5}y\right)^2$$

47. Multiply and simplify:

$$(5x + 2)(5x - 2) - (x + 3)^2$$

48. Divide and simplify:

$$\frac{6n^5 + 5n^4 + 3n^2}{n^4}$$

49. Divide:

$$\frac{y^2 - 11y + 2}{y + 3}$$

50. Divide:

$$\frac{4y^3 + 3y - 5}{2y - 1}$$

MULTIPLE CHOICE

51. Find the value of $(-3)^4$

    a.   -12
    b.   12
    c.   -81
    d.   81
    e.   none of these

52. Find the value of -5^2

    a. -10
    b. 10
    c. -25
    d. 25
    e.   none of these

53. Simplify:

$$x^6 \, x^8$$

    a. x^{14}
    b. x^{48}
    c. x^{28}
    d. $2x^{48}$
    e.   none of these

54. Simplify:

$$y^6 \cdot y \cdot y^{12}$$

    a. y^{72}
    b. y^{73}
    c. y^{18}
    d. y^{19}
    e.   none of these

55. Simplify:

$$(x^6)^{10}$$

    a. x^{16}
    b. x^{60}
    c. $6x^{10}$
    d. $10x^6$
    e.   none of these

56. Simplify:

$$(5t^6)^2$$

    a. $5t^8$
    b. $5t^{12}$
    c. $25t^8$
    d. $25t^{12}$
    e.   none of these

57. Simplify:

$$m^4 (m^3)^{12}$$

a. m^{19}
b. m^{144}
c. m^{84}
d. m^{1728}
e. none of these

58. Simplify:

$$(y^5)^3 y^8$$

a. y^{23}
b. y^{16}
c. y^{120}
d. y^{29}
e. none of these

59. Simplify:

$$(4x^3)^2 (3x^5)^3$$

a. $12x^{21}$
b. $12x^{13}$
c. $432x^{21}$
d. $432x^{90}$
e. none of these

60. Find the value of 8^0

a. 8

b. 0

c. $\frac{1}{8}$

d. 1

e. none of these

61. Simplify (assume that the variables are nonzero):

$$(5t + 3w)^0$$

a. 8
b. 2
c. 1
d. 0
e. none of these

62. Write without negative exponents:

$$y^{-8}$$

a. $\dfrac{1}{y^8}$

b. $-8y$

c. $\dfrac{1}{8y}$

d. $\dfrac{8}{y}$

e. none of these

63. Write without negative exponents:

$$(3x)^{-4}$$

a. $-12x$

b. $\dfrac{3}{x^4}$

c. $-3x^4$

d. $\dfrac{1}{(3x)^4}$

e. none of these

64. Simplify:

$$\dfrac{2^{100}}{2^{96}}$$

a. 16
b. 4
c. 1
d. 8
e. none of these

65. Simplify and write your answer without negative exponents:

$$\frac{54t^4}{18t^{12}}$$

  a. $3t^8$

  b. $\frac{3}{t^8}$

  c. $\frac{3}{t^3}$

  d. $\frac{1}{3t^3}$

  e. none of these

66. Simplify and write your answer without negative exponents:

$$\left(\frac{3y}{x^4}\right)^{-3}$$

  a. $\frac{-9x}{y^3}$

  b. $\frac{-27x^{12}}{y^3}$

  c. $\frac{-27y^3}{x^{12}}$

  d. $\frac{x^{12}}{27y^3}$

  e. none of these

67. Simplify and write your answer without negative exponents:

$$\frac{9y^{-5}}{21y^{-20}}$$

a. $\dfrac{3y^{15}}{7}$

b. $\dfrac{3}{7y^4}$

c. $\dfrac{3}{7y^{15}}$

d. $\dfrac{3y^4}{7}$

e. none of these

68. Simplify and write your answer without negative exponents:

$$\frac{(t^{-4}y^5)^{-6}}{(t\ y^4)^3}$$

a. $\dfrac{1}{t^{13}y^8}$

b. $\dfrac{y^{42}}{t^{21}}$

c. $\dfrac{t^{21}}{y^{42}}$

d. $\dfrac{t^{13}}{y^8}$

e. none of these

69. Write in scientific notation:

0.00083

a. 8.3×10^{-5}
b. 8.3×10^{5}
c. 8.3×10^{-4}
d. 8.3×10^{4}
e. none of these

64

70. Write in scientific notation:

   5360000

   a. 5.36×10^{-6}
   b. 5.36×10^6
   c. 5.36×10^{-7}
   d. 5.36×10^7
   e.   none of these

71. Multiply:

   $$-\frac{2}{3}(x^5 y^2)^4 \text{ by } (6x^2 y)^2$$

   a. $-24x^{13} y^8$
   b. $-24x^{24} y^{10}$
   c. $-24x^{80} y^{16}$
   d. $-24x^{36} y^{12}$
   e.   none of these

72. Simplify:

   $$(4a^3 b^5)(-6a^8 b)$$

   a. $-24a^{11} b^6$
   b. $-24a^{24} b^5$
   c. $-24a^{11} b^5$
   d. $-24a^{24} b^6$
   e.   none of these

73. Divide:

   $$9a^5 b^8 \text{ by } ab^2$$

   a. $9a^5 b^4$
   b. $9a^4 b^4$
   c. $9a^4 b^6$
   d. $9a^6 b^{10}$
   e.   none of these

74. Simplify:

$$\frac{(-6t^5 w^2)^2}{(2t^{12} w)(9t^8 w^{11})}$$

a. $\dfrac{-2}{3t^{13} w^8}$

b. $\dfrac{2}{t^{10} w^8}$

c. $\dfrac{-2}{3t^{13} w^7}$

d. $\dfrac{2t^{10}}{w^8}$

e. none of these

75. Simplify:

$$\frac{4m^3 x^{12}}{(2m^5 x^2)^3}$$

a. $\dfrac{x^7}{2m^5}$

b. $\dfrac{2x^7}{3m^5}$

c. $\dfrac{x^2}{2m^5}$

d. $\dfrac{2m^{18}}{3x^6}$

e. none of these

76. Which of the following is a trinomial?

a. $3x^2 y$
b. $3x^3 + 3y^3$
c. $3x^3 + 6x^2 + 9x - 3$
d. $3x^3 + 9x - 12$
e. none of these

77. Which of the following is a monomial?

a. $5x^2 y$
b. $x^2 + 1$
c. $x + y + z$
d. $4 + 3x$
e. none of these

78. Find the degree of:

$$3t^8 - 11t^{12} + 2t - 15$$

a. 21
b. -11
c. 8
d. 12
e. none of these

79. Find the degree of:

$$5x^9 - x^{10} + 30x^{12} + 40x^{20}$$

a. 20
b. 51
c. 40
d. 31
e. none of these

80. Simplify:

$$-(18x^3wt^3 - y^3) - (5m^3 + 4x^3wt^3)$$

a. $-22x^3wt^3 - y^3 - 5m^3$
b. $-28x^6w^2t^6y^3m^3$
c. $-14x^3wt^3 - y^3 - 5m^3$
d. $-22x^3wt^3 + y^3 - 5m^3$
e. none of these

81. Simplify:

$$6x^3y - 4(3t - 5xy^3) + 30t$$

a. $11x^4y^4 + 18t$
b. $11x^4y^4 + 18t^2$
c. $29x^4y^4t^2$
d. $x^2y^2 + 18t$
e. none of these

82. Add the polynomials:

$$(w^5 - 2w^3 + 3w^2 - 11) + (2w^5 + w^4 - 9w^3 + 3)$$

a. $3w^5 + w^4 - 11w^3 + 3w^2 - 8$
b. $-12w^{14}$
c. $2w^{10} + w^4 + 18w^6 + 3w^2 - 33$
d. $2w^5 + w^4 - 7w^3 + 3w^2 - 14$
e. none of these

67

83. Subtract the first polynomial from the second:

$$5x^3 + 2x^2 - 14 \quad , \quad 2x^3 - 3x + 12$$

a. $-3x^3 + 2x^2 - 3x - 2$
b. $-3x^3 - 2x^2 - 3x + 2$
c. $-3x^3 - 2x^2 - 3x - 26$
d. $-3x^3 - 2x^2 - 3x + 26$
e. none of these

84. Subtract the first polynomial from the second:

$$\tfrac{2}{3}t^5 - \tfrac{1}{2}t^3 + \tfrac{5}{8} \quad , \quad \tfrac{2}{9}t^4 - \tfrac{1}{3}t^3 + \tfrac{3}{5}t - \tfrac{2}{5}$$

a. $-\tfrac{2}{3}t^5 + \tfrac{2}{9}t^4 + \tfrac{5}{6}t^3 + \tfrac{3}{5}t + \tfrac{9}{40}$

b. $-\tfrac{2}{3}t^5 + \tfrac{2}{9}t^4 + \tfrac{1}{6}t^3 + \tfrac{3}{5}t - \tfrac{41}{40}$

c. $-\tfrac{2}{3}t^5 + \tfrac{2}{9}t^4 - t^3 + \tfrac{3}{5}t - \tfrac{7}{13}$

d. $-\tfrac{2}{3}t^5 + \tfrac{2}{9}t^4 - \tfrac{5}{6}t^3 + \tfrac{3}{5}t - \tfrac{41}{40}$

e. none of these

85. Simplify:

$$(2y^3 - 3y + 5) - (y + 5y^2 - 11) + (9 - 12y + 2y^2)$$

a. $2y^3 + 7y^2 - 16y + 3$
b. $2y^3 - 3y^2 - 16y + 3$
c. $2y^3 - 3y^2 - 16y + 25$
d. $2y^3 - 7y^2 + 8y + 7$
e. none of these

86. Simplify:

$$-5x^4 + 9x^3 - [-x^4 - (5x^3 - 11x^4)]$$

a. $11x^7$
b. $-15x^4 + 14x^3$
c. $7x^4 + 4x^3$
d. $7x^4 + 14x^3$
e. none of these

87. Multiply:

$$y^5 (y^3 - 5y^2 + 8y - 9)$$

a. $y^{15} - 5y^{10} + 8y^6 - 9y^5$
b. $y^{15} - 5y^{10} - y^5$
c. $y^8 - 5y^7 - y^5$
d. $y^8 - 5y^7 + 8y^6 - 9y^5$
e. none of these

88. Multiply:

$$-\frac{3}{4}y^3 \left[\frac{16}{9}y^4 - 8y^2 + \frac{5}{18} \right]$$

a. $-\frac{4}{3}y^7 + 6y^5 - \frac{5}{24}y^3$

b. $-\frac{4}{3}y^{12} + 6y^6 - \frac{5}{24}y^3$

c. $\frac{13}{36}y^7 - 6y^5 + \frac{1}{7}y^3$

d. $-\frac{4}{9}y^{12} + 6y^6 - \frac{5}{24}y^3$

e. none of these

89. Multiply:

$$-3w^5 t^4 (9w^3 t^2 - 8w^2 t - 4w + 12t)$$

a. $6w^8 t^6 - 11w^7 t^5 - 7w^6 t^4 + 9w^5 t^5$
b. $-27w^{15} t^8 + 24w^{10} t^4 - 24w^5 t^4$
c. $-27w^8 t^6 + 24w^7 t^5 + 12w^6 t^4 - 36w^5 t^5$
d. $-27w^8 t^6 + 24w^7 t^4 - 24w^5 t^4$
e. none of these

90. Multiply:

$$(y + 2)(y - 9)$$

a. $y^2 - 18$
b. $-6y - 18$
c. $y^2 + 7y - 18$
d. $y^2 + 11y - 18$
e. none of these

91. Multiply:

$$(t - 8)(t - 5)$$

a. $t^2 + 40$
b. $t^2 - 3t + 40$
c. $t^2 - 13t + 40$
d. $t^2 - 3t - 40$
e. none of these

92. Multiply:

$$(4y - 9)(3y + 5)$$

a. $12y^2 - 7y - 45$
b. $5y - 45$
c. $12y^2 - 45$
d. $12y^2 - 4y - 45$
e. none of these

93. Multiply:

$$(2w - 5y)(3w + 8y)$$

a. $6w^2 + 3wy - 40y^2$
b. $6w^2 + wy - 40y^2$
c. $6w^2 - 40y^2$
d. $6w^2 - 31wy - 40y^2$
e. none of these

94. Multiply:

$$(5x - 3)(4x^2 - 2x + 7)$$

a. $18x^6$
b. $20x^3 - 12x^2 + 35x - 21$
c. $20x^3 - 22x^2 + 41x - 21$
d. $20x^3 + 2x^2 + 29x - 21$
e. none of these

95. Find the product:

$$(3x + t)^2$$

a. $9x^2 + t^2$
b. $6x^2 + 3xt + t^2$
c. $9x^2 + 3xt + t^2$
d. $9x^2 + 6xt + t^2$
e. none of these

96. Find the product:

$$\left[\frac{3}{8}w - \frac{2}{3}T\right]^2$$

a. $\frac{9}{64}w^2 - \frac{4}{9}T^2$

b. $\frac{9}{64}w^2 + \frac{4}{9}T^2$

c. $\frac{9}{64}w^2 - \frac{1}{2}Tw + \frac{4}{9}T^2$

d. $\frac{9}{64}w^2 - \frac{1}{4}Tw + \frac{4}{9}T^2$

e. none of these

97. Multiply and simplify:

$$(3x + 4)(3x - 4) - (x + 6)^2$$

a. $8x^2 - 12x - 52$
b. $8x^2 - 52$
c. $8x^2 + 12x + 20$
d. $8x^2 + 20$
e. none of these

98. Divide:

$$\frac{5y^6 + 2y^4 + 8y^3 + 3y}{y^3}$$

a. $13y^3 + 2y^4 + 3y$

b. $5y^3 + 2y + 8 + \frac{3}{y^2}$

c. $5y^2 + 2y + 8 + \frac{3}{y^2}$

d. $5y^3 + 2y + 8 + 3y$

e. none of these

99. Divide:

$$\frac{x^2 - 8x + 3}{x + 2}$$

a. $-3x + 3$

b. $-3x + \frac{3}{2}$

c. $x - 6 - \frac{9}{x+2}$

d. $x - 10 - \frac{17}{x+2}$

e. none of these

100. Divide:

$$\frac{12x^3 + 5x - 3}{2x - 1}$$

a. $6x^2 + 5x - 3$

b. $6x^2 + 3x + 4 + \frac{1}{2x-1}$

c. $6x^2 - 3x + 4 - \frac{7}{2x-1}$

d. $6x^2 + \frac{11}{2}x - 8\frac{1}{2}$

e. none of these

72

1. ANS:16   TYPE:S   DIFF:1   SECT:301   OBJ:301   RAND:Y

2. ANS:-16   TYPE:S   DIFF:2   SECT:301   OBJ:301   RAND:Y

3. TYPE:S   DIFF:1   SECT:301   OBJ:302   RAND:Y

ANSWER:
    x^{14}

4. TYPE:S   DIFF:1   SECT:301   OBJ:302   RAND:Y

ANSWER:
    b^{15}

5. TYPE:S   DIFF:1   SECT:301   OBJ:303   RAND:Y

ANSWER:
    x^{20}

6. TYPE:S   DIFF:2   SECT:301   OBJ:303   RAND:Y

ANSWER:
    $64w^6$

7. TYPE:S   DIFF:2   SECT:301   OBJ:305   RAND:Y

ANSWER:
    y^{25}

8. TYPE:S   DIFF:2   SECT:301   OBJ:305   RAND:Y

ANSWER:
    x^{22}

9. TYPE:S   DIFF:3   SECT:301   OBJ:305   RAND:Y

ANSWER:
    $200x^{14}$

10. ANS:1   TYPE:S   DIFF:1   SECT:301   OBJ:304   RAND:Y

11. ANS:1   TYPE:S   DIFF:2   SECT:301   OBJ:304   RAND:Y

12. TYPE:S DIFF:1 SECT:302 OBJ:306 RAND:Y

ANSWER:
$$\frac{1}{x^3}$$

13. TYPE:S DIFF:2 SECT:302 OBJ:306 RAND:Y

ANSWER:
$$\frac{1}{(2x)^5}$$

14. ANS:9 TYPE:S DIFF:1 SECT:302 OBJ:307 RAND:Y

15. TYPE:S DIFF:1 SECT:302 OBJ:307 RAND:Y

ANSWER:
$$\frac{3}{y^3}$$

16. TYPE:S DIFF:2 SECT:302 OBJ:306 RAND:Y

ANSWER:
$$\frac{z^8}{16x^4}$$

17. TYPE:S DIFF:2 SECT:302 OBJ:307 RAND:Y

ANSWER:
$$\frac{x^6}{4}$$

18. TYPE:S DIFF:3 SECT:302 OBJ:307 RAND:Y

ANSWER:
$$\frac{x^2}{w^{17}}$$

19. TYPE:S DIFF:2 SECT:302 OBJ:308 RAND:Y

ANSWER:
    3.6×10^{-3}

20. TYPE:S DIFF:2 SECT:302 OBJ:308 RAND:Y

ANSWER:
2.95002×10^5

21. TYPE:S DIFF:3 SECT:303 OBJ:309 RAND:Y

ANSWER:
$-60x^8 y^{16}$

22. TYPE:S DIFF:2 SECT:303 OBJ:309 RAND:Y

ANSWER:
$-15x^8 y^3$

23. ANS:5a TYPE:S DIFF:1 SECT:303 OBJ:310 RAND:Y

24. TYPE:S DIFF:3 SECT:303 OBJ:310 RAND:Y

ANSWER:
$$\frac{4}{3x^3 y^3}$$

25. TYPE:S DIFF:2 SECT:303 OBJ:310 RAND:Y

ANSWER:
$$\frac{3y^7}{4x^{10}}$$

26. ANS:trinomial TYPE:S DIFF:2 SECT:304 OBJ:311 RAND:Y

27. ANS:monomial TYPE:S DIFF:2 SECT:304 OBJ:311 RAND:Y

28. ANS:8 TYPE:S DIFF:2 SECT:304 OBJ:312 RAND:Y

29. ANS:5 TYPE:S DIFF:2 SECT:304 OBJ:312 RAND:Y

30. TYPE:S DIFF:2 SECT:304 OBJ:313 RAND:Y

ANSWER:
$-14x^2 yz^4 + z^5 - 3x^2$

75

31. TYPE:S DIFF:2 SECT:304 OBJ:313 RAND:Y

ANSWER:
   $5a^2b - 6ab^2 + 21$

32. TYPE:S DIFF:2 SECT:305 OBJ:314 RAND:Y

ANSWER:
   $4x^4 + x^3 - 3x^2 - 3x - 2$

33. TYPE:S DIFF:2 SECT:305 OBJ:315 RAND:Y

ANSWER:
   $-2t^3 - 8t^2 + 11t + 9$

34. TYPE:S DIFF:3 SECT:305 OBJ:315 RAND:Y

ANSWER:
   $-\frac{3}{4}z^4 + \frac{1}{4}z^3 + \frac{1}{2}z^2 + \frac{1}{2}z - \frac{23}{24}$

35. TYPE:S DIFF:2 SECT:305 OBJ:316 RAND:Y

ANSWER:
   $3r^3 + 6r^2 - 6r + 16$

36. TYPE:S DIFF:3 SECT:305 OBJ:316 RAND:Y

ANSWER:
   $-15x^5 + 5x^3$

37. TYPE:S DIFF:1 SECT:306 OBJ:317 RAND:Y

ANSWER:
   $x^7 - 3x^6 + 9x^5 - 3x^4$

38. TYPE:S DIFF:2 SECT:306 OBJ:317 RAND:Y

ANSWER:
   $-\frac{3}{4}y^5 + 4y^4 - \frac{3}{5}$

39. TYPE:S DIFF:3 SECT:306 OBJ:317 RAND:Y

ANSWER:
   $15w^6t^8 - 10w^5t^5 - 15w^3t^3 + 55w^2t^4$

40. TYPE:S DIFF:1 SECT:306 OBJ:318 RAND:Y

ANSWER:
$x^2 - 2x - 15$

41. TYPE:S DIFF:1 SECT:306 OBJ:318 RAND:Y

ANSWER:
$y^2 - 9y + 18$

42. TYPE:S DIFF:2 SECT:306 OBJ:318 RAND:Y

ANSWER:
$10y^2 - 11y - 6$

43. TYPE:S DIFF:2 SECT:306 OBJ:318 RAND:Y

ANSWER:
$15n^2 - 32ny - 7y^2$

44. TYPE:S DIFF:3 SECT:306 OBJ:318 RAND:Y

ANSWER:
$10t^3 - 47t^2 + t + 36$

45. TYPE:S DIFF:2 SECT:307 OBJ:319 RAND:Y

ANSWER:
$16a^2 + 8ab + b^2$

46. TYPE:S DIFF:3 SECT:307 OBJ:319 RAND:Y

ANSWER:
$\frac{4}{9}x^2 - \frac{4}{5}xy + \frac{9}{25}y^2$

47. TYPE:S DIFF:3 SECT:307 OBJ:319 RAND:Y

ANSWER:
$24x^2 - 6x - 13$

48. TYPE:S DIFF:2 SECT:308 OBJ:320 RAND:Y

ANSWER:
$6n + 5 + \frac{3}{n^2}$

77

49. TYPE:S DIFF:2 SECT:308 OBJ:321 RAND:Y

ANSWER:

$$y - 14 + \frac{44}{y+3}$$

50. TYPE:S DIFF:3 SECT:308 OBJ:321 RAND:Y

ANSWER:

$$2y^2 + y + 2 - \frac{3}{2y-1}$$

51. ANS:d TYPE:M DIFF:1 SECT:301 OBJ:301 RAND:Y

52. ANS:c TYPE:M DIFF:2 SECT:301 OBJ:301 RAND:Y

53. ANS:a TYPE:M DIFF:1 SECT:301 OBJ:302 RAND:Y

54. ANS:d TYPE:M DIFF:1 SECT:301 OBJ:302 RAND:Y

55. ANS:b TYPE:M DIFF:1 SECT:301 OBJ:303 RAND:Y

56. ANS:d TYPE:M DIFF:2 SECT:301 OBJ:303 RAND:Y

57. ANS:e TYPE:M DIFF:2 SECT:301 OBJ:305 RAND:Y

58. ANS:a TYPE:M DIFF:2 SECT:301 OBJ:305 RAND:Y

59. ANS:c TYPE:M DIFF:3 SECT:301 OBJ:305 RAND:Y

60. ANS:d TYPE:M DIFF:1 SECT:301 OBJ:304 RAND:Y

61. ANS:c TYPE:M DIFF:2 SECT:301 OBJ:304 RAND:Y

62. ANS:a TYPE:M DIFF:1 SECT:302 OBJ:306 RAND:Y

63. ANS:d TYPE:M DIFF:2 SECT:302 OBJ:306 RAND:Y

64. ANS:a TYPE:M DIFF:1 SECT:302 OBJ:307 RAND:Y

65. ANS:b TYPE:M DIFF:1 SECT:302 OBJ:307 RAND:Y

66. ANS:d TYPE:M DIFF:2 SECT:302 OBJ:306 RAND:Y

67. ANS:a TYPE:M DIFF:2 SECT:302 OBJ:307 RAND:Y

68. ANS:c TYPE:M DIFF:3 SECT:302 OBJ:307 RAND:Y

69. ANS:c TYPE:M DIFF:2 SECT:302 OBJ:308 RAND:Y

70. ANS:b TYPE:M DIFF:2 SECT:302 OBJ:308 RAND:Y

71. ANS:b TYPE:M DIFF:3 SECT:303 OBJ:309 RAND:Y

72. ANS:a TYPE:M DIFF:2 SECT:303 OBJ:309 RAND:Y

73. ANS:c TYPE:M DIFF:1 SECT:303 OBJ:310 RAND:Y

74. ANS:b TYPE:M DIFF:3 SECT:303 OBJ:310 RAND:Y

75. ANS:e TYPE:M DIFF:2 SECT:303 OBJ:310 RAND:Y

76. ANS:d TYPE:M DIFF:2 SECT:304 OBJ:311 RAND:Y

77. ANS:a TYPE:M DIFF:2 SECT:304 OBJ:311 RAND:Y

78. ANS:d TYPE:M DIFF:2 SECT:304 OBJ:312 RAND:Y

79. ANS:a TYPE:M DIFF:2 SECT:304 OBJ:312 RAND:Y

80. ANS:d TYPE:M DIFF:2 SECT:304 OBJ:313 RAND:Y

81. ANS:e TYPE:M DIFF:2 SECT:304 OBJ:313 RAND:Y

82. ANS:a TYPE:M DIFF:2 SECT:305 OBJ:314 RAND:Y

83. ANS:d   TYPE:M   DIFF:2   SECT:305   OBJ:315   RAND:Y

84. ANS:b   TYPE:M   DIFF:3   SECT:305   OBJ:315   RAND:Y

85. ANS:c   TYPE:M   DIFF:2   SECT:305   OBJ:316   RAND:Y

86. ANS:b   TYPE:M   DIFF:3   SECT:305   OBJ:316   RAND:Y

87. ANS:d   TYPE:M   DIFF:1   SECT:306   OBJ:317   RAND:Y

88. ANS:a   TYPE:M   DIFF:2   SECT:306   OBJ:317   RAND:Y

89. ANS:c   TYPE:M   DIFF:3   SECT:306   OBJ:317   RAND:Y

90. ANS:e   TYPE:M   DIFF:1   SECT:306   OBJ:318   RAND:Y

91. ANS:c   TYPE:M   DIFF:1   SECT:306   OBJ:318   RAND:Y

92. ANS:a   TYPE:M   DIFF:2   SECT:306   OBJ:318   RAND:Y

93. ANS:b   TYPE:M   DIFF:2   SECT:306   OBJ:318   RAND:Y

94. ANS:c   TYPE:M   DIFF:3   SECT:306   OBJ:318   RAND:Y

95. ANS:d   TYPE:M   DIFF:2   SECT:307   OBJ:319   RAND:Y

96. ANS:c   TYPE:M   DIFF:3   SECT:307   OBJ:319   RAND:Y

97. ANS:a   TYPE:M   DIFF:3   SECT:307   OBJ:319   RAND:Y

98. ANS:b   TYPE:M   DIFF:2   SECT:308   OBJ:320   RAND:Y

99. ANS:e   TYPE:M   DIFF:2   SECT:308   OBJ:321   RAND:Y

100. ANS:b   TYPE:M   DIFF:3   SECT:308   OBJ:321   RAND:Y

CHAPTER 4: FACTORING

SHORT ANSWER

1. Determine if the number is composite or prime:

　　　37

2. Factor into primes:

　　　84

3. Factor into primes:

　　　72

4. Find the missing factor:

　　$12x^6 = 2x^2 (\ ? \ )$

5. Factor out the greatest common factor:

　　$12x^7 - 6x^5 + 9x^3$

6. Factor out the greatest common factor:

　　$10y^5 - 5y^3 + 20y^2$

7. Factor out the greatest common factor:

　　$30w^6 z^4 + 12w^5 z^3 - 18w^2 z^4 + 6w^2 z^3$

8. Factor completely. If the polynomial is prime, write "prime."

　　$b^2 + 11b + 24$

9. Factor completely. If the polynomial is prime, write "prime."

　　$x^2 + 2xy - 15y^2$

10. Factor completely. If the polynomial is prime, write "prime."

　　$w^2 - 11w + 30$

11. Factor completely. If the polynomial is prime, write "prime."

　　$a^2 - 7at - 18t^2$

12. Factor completely. If the polynomial is prime, write "prime."

　　$x^3 - 3x^2 - 40x$

13. Factor completely. If the polynomial is prime, write "prime."

　　$2c^4 + 18c^3 - 44c^2$

14. Factor completely. If the polynomial is prime, write "prime."

$2w^2 - w - 15$

15. Factor completely. If the polynomial is prime, write "prime."

$3w^2 + 26w - 9$

16. Factor completely. If the polynomial is prime, write "prime."

$6w^2 - w - 12$

17. Factor completely. If the polynomial is prime, write "prime."

$6u^3 + 2u^2 - 20u$

18. Factor completely. If the polynomial is prime, write "prime."

$10x^7 + 29x^6 - 21x^5$

19. Factor completely. If the polynomial is prime, write "prime."

$x^2 - 36$

20. Factor completely. If the polynomial is prime, write "prime."

$y^2 + 9$

21. Factor completely. If the polynomial is prime, write "prime."

$4p^2 - 25q^2$

22. Factor completely. If the polynomial is prime, write "prime."

$m^2 - 8m + 16$

23. Factor completely. If the polynomial is prime, write "prime."

$y^2 - 2hy + h^2$

24. Factor completely. If the polynomial is prime, write "prime."

$w^3 - 27$

25. Factor completely. If the polynomial is prime, write "prime."

$v^3 + 64$

26. Factor completely. If the polynomial is prime, write "prime."

$8x^3 - 125w^3$

27. Factor completely. If the polynomial is prime, write "prime."

$$c^3 - \frac{1}{8}$$

28. Factor completely. If the polynomial is prime, write "prime."

$$x(y + w) - 2(y + w)$$

29. Factor completely. If the polynomial is prime, write "prime."

$$sw + 5s + tw + 5t$$

30. Factor completely. If the polynomial is prime, write "prime."

$$ax^2 + bx^2 - ay^2 - by^2$$

31. Factor completely. If the polynomial is prime, write "prime."

$$w^2 x + 3w^2 - 9x - 27$$

32. Factor completely. If the polynomial is prime, write "prime."

$$3w^2 - 27$$

33. Factor completely. If the polynomial is prime, write "prime."

$$ax^3 - a$$

34. Factor completely. If the polynomial is prime, write "prime."

$$wx^3 + tx^3 - wy^3 - ty^3$$

35. Factor completely. If the polynomial is prime, write "prime."

$$5y^4 + 25y^3 + 20y^2$$

36. Solve:

$$(y + 2)(3y - 4) = 0$$

37. Solve:

$$3w(w + 8) = 0$$

38. Solve:

$$b^2 - 7b - 18 = 0$$

39. Solve:

$$2b^2 - 11b - 21 = 0$$

40. Solve:

$$3x^2 - 22x - 16 = 0$$

41. Solve:

$$2x = 8x^2$$

42. Solve:

$$(3x - 2)(x + 1) = 8$$

43. Solve:

$$(2y + 3)(y - 2) = y + 6$$

44. Solve:

$$9x^3 - 25x = 0$$

45. Solve:

$$2x^3 = x(5x + 12)$$

ESSAY

46. Two consecutive integers have the property that the sum of their squares is 41. Find the two integers.

47. The length of a rectangle is one foot more than twice the width. If the area of the rectangle is 15 square feet, find the length and width of the rectangle.

48. The base of a triangle is one foot less than three times the height. If the area is 2 square feet, find the base and the height of the triangle.

49. One leg of a right triangle is two inches longer than the other leg. If the hypotenuse is 10 inches, find the lengths of the two legs.

50. The length of the hypotenuse of a right triangle is 10 inches less than twice the length of the shorter leg. If the length of the other leg is 10 inches more than the length of the shorter leg, find the length of the hypotenuse.

85

51. Which of the following numbers is composite?

    a. 53
    b. 83
    c. 103
    d. 123
    e. none of these

52. Factor into primes:

        126

    a. $2 \cdot 63$
    b. $2 \cdot 9 \cdot 7$
    c. $2 \cdot 3 \cdot 21$
    d. $3 \cdot 6 \cdot 7$
    e. none of these

53. Factor into primes:

        105

    a. $3 \cdot 35$
    b $3 \cdot 5 \cdot 7$
    c. $7 \cdot 15$
    d. $5 \cdot 21$
    e. none of these

54. Find the missing factor:

        $15y^8 = 3y^4 \ (\ ? \ )$

    a. $5y^2$
    b. $5y^4$
    c. y^5
    d. y^{20}
    e. none of these

55. Factor out the greatest common factor:

        $12x^8 - 8x^6 + 20x^5$

    a. $2x(6x^7 - 4x^5 + 10x^4)$
    b. $4x^4(3x^4 - 2x^2 + 5x)$
    c. $4x^5(3x^3 - 2x + 5)$
    d. $2x^3(6x^5 - 4x^3 + 10x^2)$
    e. none of these

86

56. Factor out the greatest common factor:

$$24x^8 - 6x^6 + 30x^2$$

a. $6x^2(4x^6 - x^4 + 5)$
b. $6x^2(4x^4 - x^3 + 5)$
c. $3x^2(8x^6 - 2x^4 + 5)$
d. $3x^2(8x^4 - 2x^3 + 5)$
e. none of these

57. Factor out the greatest common factor:

$$30w^{12}y^2 - 50w^8y^4 + 20w^4y^{11} + 10w^4y$$

a. $2wy(15w^{11}y - 25w^7y^3 + 10w^3y^{10} + 5w^3)$
b. $10w^4y(3w^3y^2 - 5w^2y^4 + 2wy^{11} + wy)$
c. $10w^4y(3w^8y - 5w^4y^3 + 2y^{10})$
d. $10w^4y(3w^8y - 5w^4y^3 + 2y^{10} + 1)$
e. none of these

58. When $y^2 - 9y + 20$ is completely factored, one of the factors is:

a. $(y + 5)$
b. y
c. $(y - 5)$
d. $(y + 20)$
e. none of these

59. When $w^2 + 6wy - 16y^2$ is completely factored, one of the factors is:

a. $(w + 8y)$
b. $(w - 8y)$
c. $(w - 16y)$
d. $(w - y)$
e. none of these

60. When $t^2 + 23t + 60$ is completely factored, one of the factors is:

a. $(t + 60)$
b. $(t + 20)$
c. $(t + 12)$
d. $(t + 4)$
e. none of these

61. When $c^2 - 10cw - 24w^2$ is completely factored, one of the factors is:

a. $(c - 24w)$
b. $(c - 6w)$
c. $(c - 4w)$
d. $(c - 12w)$
e. none of these

62. When $x^3 + 7x^2 - 30x$ is completely factored, one of the factors is:

    a. $(x^2 - 3x)$
    b. $(x + 3)$
    c. $(x + 10)$
    d. $(x^2 + 10x)$
    e. none of these

63. When $3x^4 + 12x^3 - 36x^2$ is completely factored, one of the factors is:

    a. $(x - 2)$
    b. $(x + 2)$
    c. $(3x^2 - 6x)$
    d. $(x^2 + 6x)$
    e. none of these

64. When $3y^2 + 4y - 4$ is completely factored, one of the factors is:

    a. $(3y + 2)$
    b. $(3y - 2)$
    c. $(3y - 4)$
    d. $(y - 4)$
    e. none of these

65. When $2w^2 + w - 21$ is completely factored, one of the factors is:

    a. $(2w + 3)$
    b. $(2w - 3)$
    c. $(w + 7)$
    d. $(w - 7)$
    e. none of these

66. When $8t^2 + 2t - 15$ is completely factored, one of the factors is:

    a. $(8t - 5)$
    b. $(4t + 5)$
    c. $(2t + 3)$
    d. $(t - 3)$
    e. none of these

67. When $6w^3 + 45w^2 - 24w$ is completely factored, one of the factors is:

    a. $(w + 8)$
    b. $(6w + 1)$
    c. $(2w + 1)$
    d. $(3w^2 + 24w)$
    e. none of these

68. When $6y^6 + 11y^5 - 10y^4$ is completely factored, one of the factors is:

    a. $(2y^3 + 5y^2)$
    b. $(y - 10)$
    c. $(2y - 5)$
    d. $(3y - 2)$
    e. none of these

69. When $t^2 - 81$ is completely factored, one of the factors is:

    a. $(t + 3)$
    b. $(t + 9)$
    c. $(t + 81)$
    d. $(t^2 + 9)$
    e. none of these

70. $x^2 + 36 =$

    a. $(x + 36)(x + 1)$
    b. $(x + 6)(x - 6)$
    c. $(x^2 + 6x)(x + 6)$
    d. $(x + 6)(x + 6)$
    e. none of these

71. $9x^2 - 16t^2 =$

    a. $(3x - 4t)^2$
    b. $(3x + 2t)(3x - 8t)$
    c. $(9x - 16t)(9x + 16t)$
    d. $(3x + 4t)(3x - 4t)$
    e. none of these

72. $y^2 - 10y + 25 =$

    a. $(y - 5)^2$
    b. $(y + 5)^2$
    c. $(y + 25)(y + 1)$
    d. $(y - 25)(y - 1)$
    e. none of these

73. $m^2 - 4lm + 4l^2 =$

    a. $(m - 2)^2$
    b. $(m + 4l)(m + 1)$
    c. $(m - 2l)^2$
    d. $(m - 4l)(m - 1)$
    e. none of these

74. When $x^3 - 64$ is completely factored, one of the factors is:

    a. $(x + 4)$
    b. $(x^2 - 4x - 16)$
    c. $(x^2 + 4x - 16)$
    d. $(x^2 + 4x + 16)$
    e. none of these

75. When $8 + y^3$ is completely factored, one of the factors is:

    a. $(2 - 2y + y^2)$
    b. $(4 - 2y + y^2)$
    c. $(4 + 2y + y^2)$
    d. $(2 + 2y + y^2)$
    e. none of these

76. When $125t^3 - 64w^3$ is completely factored, one of the factors is:

    a. $(5t - 4w)$
    b. $(25t - 8w)$
    c. $(5t^2 + 20tw + 4w^2)$
    d. $(5t^2 + 20t + 4)$
    e. none of these

77. When $M^3 - \dfrac{1}{125}$ is completely factored, one of the factors is:

    a. $(M + 5)$

    b. $(M - 5)$

    c. $\left[M^2 + \dfrac{1}{25}M + \dfrac{1}{25}\right]$

    d. $\left[M^2 + \dfrac{1}{5}M + \dfrac{1}{25}\right]$

    e. none of these

78. $A(B + C) + N(B + C) =$

    a. $AN(B + C)$
    b. $(A + N)(B + C)^2$
    c. $(A + N)(B + C)$
    d. $(AN)(BC)$
    e. none of these

79. When $ax + 5a + lx + 5l$ is completely factored, one of the factors is:

    a. x
    b. a
    c. $(a + x)$
    d. $(a + l)$
    e. none of these

80. When $xw^2 + yw^2 - xm^2 - ym^2$ is completely factored, one of the factors is:

   a. $(w + m)$
   b. $(w^2 - m^2)$
   c. $(w^2 + m^2)$
   d. $(xw - my)$
   e. none of these

81. When $t^2y + 5t^2 - 4y - 20$ is completely factored, one of the factors is:

   a. $(t^2 - 4)$
   b. $(y - 5)$
   c. $(y + 5)$
   d. $(5y + t^2)$
   e. none of these

82. When $2x^2 - 8$ is completely factored, one of the factors is:

   a. $(2x - 4)$
   b. $(2x + 4)$
   c. $(x + 8)$
   d. $(x - 8)$
   e. none of these

83. $yt^3 - y =$

   a. $y(t - 1)^3$
   b. $(yt^2 - 1)(t + y)$
   c. $y(t - 1)(t^2 + t - 1)$
   d. $y(t - 1)(t^2 + t + 1)$
   e. none of these

84. $ab^3 + xb^3 - ac^3 - xc^3 =$

   a. $(a + x)^2 (b - c)^3$
   b. $(a + x)(b - c)^3$
   c. $(a + x)(b - c)(b^2 + bc + c^2)$
   d. $(a + x)(b - c)(b + c)^2$
   e. none of these

85. When $3x^4 + 30x^3 + 48x^2$ is completely factored, one of the factors is:

   a. $(x + 8)$
   b. $(x^2 + 2x)$
   c. $(3x + 6)$
   d. $(x + 16)$
   e. none of these

86. Solve:

$$(w + 3)(5w - 6) = 0$$

a. $w = 3$ or $w = -\frac{6}{5}$

b. $w = -3$ or $w = \frac{6}{5}$

c. $w = -3$ or $w = 1$

d. $w = 3$ or $w = 1$

e. none of these

87. Solve:

$$2x(x + 5) = 0$$

a. $x = 2$ or $x = -5$
b. $x = 2$ or $x = 5$
c. $x = 5$ only
d. $x = -5$ only
e. none of these

88. When you solve $x^2 - 7x - 30 = 0$, you will find that:

a. all the solutions are between -1 and 30
b. all the solutions are between -6 and 15
c. all the solutions are between -20 and 6
d. all the solutions are between -30 and 1
e. none of these

89. When you solve $3x^2 - 2x - 16 = 0$, you will find that:

a. all the solutions are between -3 and 3
b. all the solutions are between -8 and 2
c. all the solutions are between -1 and 16
d. all the solutions are between -16 and 1
e. none of these

90. When you solve $5x^2 + 8x - 4 = 0$, you will find that:

a. all the solutions are between -1 and 10
b. all the solutions are between -10 and 1
c. all the solutions are between 0 and 14
d. all the solutions are between -14 and 0
e. none of these

91. When you solve $3y = 12y^2$, you will find that:

    a. all the solutions are between 1 and 2
    b. all the solutions are between -1 and 1
    c. all the solutions are between 3 and 5
    d. all the solutions are between -5 and -3
    e. none of these

92. When you solve $(5x - 3)(x + 1) = 36$, you will find that:

    a. all the solutions are between -2 and 6
    b. all the solutions are between -8 and 1
    c. all the solutions are between -5 and 4
    d. all the solutions are between -1 and 20
    e. none of these

93. When you solve $(3y - 8)(y + 5) = 2(8y + 7)$, you will find that:

    a. all the solutions are between -5 1/2 and 4
    b. all the solutions are between -4 and 5 1/2
    c. all the solutions are between -1 and 10
    d. all the solutions are between -3 1/2 and 8
    e. none of these

94. Solve:

$$4x^3 - 9x = 0$$

    a. $\left\{\dfrac{3}{2}\right\}$

    b. $\left\{-\dfrac{3}{2},\ \dfrac{3}{2}\right\}$

    c. $\left\{\dfrac{9}{4}\right\}$

    d. $\left\{-\dfrac{9}{4},\ 0,\ \dfrac{9}{4}\right\}$

    e. none of these

95. Solve:

$$3x^3 = x(5x - 28)$$

a. $\left\{-4,\ 0,\ \dfrac{7}{3}\right\}$

b. $\left\{0,\ \dfrac{28}{5}\right\}$

c. $\left\{-\dfrac{7}{3},\ 0,\ 4\right\}$

d. $\left\{-\dfrac{28}{5},\ 0\right\}$

e. none of these

96. Two consecutive even integers have the property that the sum of their squares is 52. Find the two integers.

a. 24, 26
b. -6, 4
c. -4, 6
d. 12, 14
e. none of these

97. The length of a rectangle is one foot less than twice the width. If the area of the rectangle is 36 square feet, find the length of the rectangle.

a. 8 feet
b. 9 feet
c. 10 feet
d. 18 1/2 feet
e. none of these

98. The base of a triangle is 4 feet longer than the height. If the area is 30 square feet, find the length of the triangle.

a. 26 feet
b. 10 feet
c. 6 feet
d. 14 feet
e. none of these

99. One leg of a right triangle is three inches longer than the other leg. If the hypotenuse is 14 inches, which of the following equations could be used to find the length of the shorter leg?

a. $x + x + 3 = 14$
b. $(x + x + 3)^2 = (14)^2$
c. $x^2 + (x + 3)^2 = 14$
d. $x^2 + (x + 3)^2 = (14)^2$
e. none of these

100. The length of the hypotenuse of a right triangle is 8 inches more than the length of the shorter leg. If the length of the other leg is 7 inches more than the length of the shorter leg, find the length of the shorter leg.

    a. 1 inch
    b. 5 inches
    c. 13 inches
    d. 15 inches
    e. none of these

1. ANS:prime TYPE:S DIFF:1 SECT:401 OBJ:401 RAND:Y

2. TYPE:S DIFF:2 SECT:401 OBJ:402 RAND:Y

ANSWER:
$2^2 \cdot 3 \cdot 7$

3. TYPE:S DIFF:2 SECT:401 OBJ:402 RAND:Y

ANSWER:
$2^3 \cdot 3^2$

4. TYPE:S DIFF:1 SECT:401 OBJ:403 RAND:Y

ANSWER:
$6x^4$

5. TYPE:S DIFF:2 SECT:401 OBJ:404 RAND:Y

ANSWER:
$3x^3 (4x^4 - 2x^2 + 3)$

6. TYPE:S DIFF:2 SECT:401 OBJ:404 RAND:Y

ANSWER:
$5y^2 (2y^3 - y + 4)$

7. TYPE:S DIFF:3 SECT:401 OBJ:404 RAND:Y

ANSWER:
$6w^2 z^3 (5w^4 z + 2w^3 - 3z + 1)$

8. TYPE:S DIFF:2 SECT:402 OBJ:405 RAND:Y

ANSWER:
$(b + 3)(b + 8)$

9. TYPE:S DIFF:3 SECT:402 OBJ:405 RAND:Y

ANSWER:
$(x - 3y)(x + 5y)$

10. TYPE:**S** DIFF:**2** SECT:**402** OBJ:**405** RAND:**Y**

ANSWER:
     $(w - 5)(w - 6)$

11. TYPE:**S** DIFF:**3** SECT:**402** OBJ:**405** RAND:**Y**

ANSWER:
     $(a + 2t)(a - 9t)$

12. TYPE:**S** DIFF:**2** SECT:**402** OBJ:**406** RAND:**Y**

ANSWER:
     $x(x + 5)(x - 8)$

13. TYPE:**S** DIFF:**2** SECT:**402** OBJ:**406** RAND:**Y**

ANSWER:
     $2c^2(c - 2)(c + 11)$

14. TYPE:**S** DIFF:**2** SECT:**403** OBJ:**407** RAND:**Y**

ANSWER:
     $(2w + 5)(w - 3)$

15. TYPE:**S** DIFF:**2** SECT:**403** OBJ:**407** RAND:**Y**

ANSWER:
     $(3w - 1)(w + 9)$

16. TYPE:**S** DIFF:**3** SECT:**403** OBJ:**407** RAND:**Y**

ANSWER:
     $(2w - 3)(3w + 4)$

17. TYPE:**S** DIFF:**2** SECT:**403** OBJ:**408** RAND:**Y**

ANSWER:
     $2u(3u - 5)(u + 2)$

18. TYPE:**S** DIFF:**3** SECT:**403** OBJ:**408** RAND:**Y**

ANSWER:
     $x^5(5x - 3)(2x + 7)$

19. TYPE:S DIFF:1 SECT:404 OBJ:409 RAND:Y

ANSWER:
    $(x + 6)(x - 6)$

20. ANS:prime TYPE:S DIFF:2 SECT:404 OBJ:410 RAND:Y

21. TYPE:S DIFF:2 SECT:404 OBJ:409 RAND:Y

ANSWER:
    $(2p - 5q)(2p + 5q)$

22. TYPE:S DIFF:2 SECT:404 OBJ:411 RAND:Y

ANSWER:
    $(m - 4)^2$

23. TYPE:S DIFF:3 SECT:404 OBJ:411 RAND:Y

ANSWER:
    $(y - h)^2$

24. TYPE:S DIFF:2 SECT:404 OBJ:412 RAND:Y

ANSWER:
    $(w - 3)(w^2 + 3w + 9)$

25. TYPE:S DIFF:2 SECT:404 OBJ:412 RAND:Y

ANSWER:
    $(v + 4)(v^2 - 4v + 16)$

26. TYPE:S DIFF:3 SECT:404 OBJ:412 RAND:Y

ANSWER:
    $(2x - 5w)(4x^2 + 10wx + 25w^2)$

27. TYPE:S DIFF:3 SECT:404 OBJ:412 RAND:Y

ANSWER:
    $\left[c - \frac{1}{2}\right]\left[c^2 + \frac{1}{2}c + \frac{1}{4}\right]$

28. TYPE:S   DIFF:2   SECT:405   OBJ:413   RAND:Y

ANSWER:
$(y + w)(x - 2)$

29. TYPE:S   DIFF:2   SECT:405   OBJ:414   RAND:Y

ANSWER:
$(s + t)(w + 5)$

30. TYPE:S   DIFF:3   SECT:405   OBJ:414   RAND:Y

ANSWER:
$(x + y)(x - y)(a + b)$

31. TYPE:S   DIFF:3   SECT:405   OBJ:414   RAND:Y

ANSWER:
$(w + 3)(w - 3)(x + 3)$

32. TYPE:S   DIFF:2   SECT:405   OBJ:415   RAND:Y

ANSWER:
$3(w + 3)(w - 3)$

33. TYPE:S   DIFF:2   SECT:405   OBJ:415   RAND:Y

ANSWER:
$a(x - 1)(x^2 + x + 1)$

34. TYPE:S   DIFF:3   SECT:405   OBJ:415   RAND:Y

ANSWER:
$(x - y)(x^2 + xy + y^2)(w + t)$

35. TYPE:S   DIFF:2   SECT:405   OBJ:415   RAND:Y

ANSWER:
$5y^2(y + 4)(y + 1)$

36. TYPE:S   DIFF:1   SECT:406   OBJ:416   RAND:Y

ANSWER:
$y = -2$ or $y = \frac{4}{3}$

37. TYPE:S DIFF:1 SECT:406 OBJ:416 RAND:Y

ANSWER:
$w = 0$ or $w = -8$

38. TYPE:S DIFF:1 SECT:406 OBJ:416 RAND:Y

ANSWER:
$b = 9$ or $b = -2$

39. TYPE:S DIFF:2 SECT:406 OBJ:416 RAND:Y

ANSWER:
$b = -\frac{3}{2}$ or $b = 7$

40. TYPE:S DIFF:2 SECT:406 OBJ:416 RAND:Y

ANSWER:
$x = -\frac{2}{3}$ or $x = 8$

41. TYPE:S DIFF:2 SECT:406 OBJ:416 RAND:Y

ANSWER:
$x = 0$ or $x = \frac{1}{4}$

42. TYPE:S DIFF:3 SECT:406 OBJ:416 RAND:Y

ANSWER:
$x = -2$ or $x = \frac{5}{3}$

43. TYPE:S DIFF:3 SECT:406 OBJ:416 RAND:Y

ANSWER:
$y = 3$ or $y = -2$

44. TYPE:S DIFF:2 SECT:406 OBJ:417 RAND:Y

ANSWER:
$x = 0$ or $x = -\frac{5}{3}$ or $x = \frac{5}{3}$

45. TYPE:**S** DIFF:**3** SECT:**406** OBJ:**417** RAND:**Y**

ANSWER:
$$x = 0 \text{ or } x = -\frac{3}{2} \text{ or } x = 4$$

46. TYPE:**E** DIFF:**2** SECT:**407** OBJ:**418** RAND:**Y**

ANSWER:
-5 and -4 or 4 and 5

47. TYPE:**E** DIFF:**2** SECT:**407** OBJ:**418** RAND:**Y**

ANSWER:
length = 6 ft and width = 2 1/2 feet

48. TYPE:**E** DIFF:**2** SECT:**407** OBJ:**418** RAND:**Y**

ANSWER:
base = 3 feet and height = 1 1/3 feet

49. TYPE:**E** DIFF:**2** SECT:**407** OBJ:**419** RAND:**Y**

ANSWER:
6 inches and 8 inches

50. ANS:**50 inches** TYPE:**E** DIFF:**3** SECT:**407** OBJ:**419** RAND:**Y**

51. ANS:**d** TYPE:**M** DIFF:**1** SECT:**401** OBJ:**401** RAND:**Y**

52. ANS:**e** TYPE:**M** DIFF:**2** SECT:**401** OBJ:**402** RAND:**Y**

53. ANS:**b** TYPE:**M** DIFF:**2** SECT:**401** OBJ:**402** RAND:**Y**

54. ANS:**b** TYPE:**M** DIFF:**1** SECT:**401** OBJ:**403** RAND:**Y**

55. ANS:**c** TYPE:**M** DIFF:**2** SECT:**401** OBJ:**404** RAND:**Y**

56. ANS:**a** TYPE:**M** DIFF:**2** SECT:**401** OBJ:**404** RAND:**Y**

57. ANS:**d** TYPE:**M** DIFF:**3** SECT:**401** OBJ:**404** RAND:**Y**

58. ANS:c TYPE:M DIFF:2 SECT:402 OBJ:405 RAND:Y

59. ANS:a TYPE:M DIFF:3 SECT:402 OBJ:405 RAND:Y

60. ANS:b TYPE:M DIFF:2 SECT:402 OBJ:405 RAND:Y

61. ANS:d TYPE:M DIFF:3 SECT:402 OBJ:405 RAND:Y

62. ANS:c TYPE:M DIFF:2 SECT:402 OBJ:406 RAND:Y

63. ANS:a TYPE:M DIFF:2 SECT:402 OBJ:406 RAND:Y

64. ANS:b TYPE:M DIFF:2 SECT:403 OBJ:407 RAND:Y

65. ANS:e TYPE:M DIFF:2 SECT:403 OBJ:407 RAND:Y

66. ANS:c TYPE:M DIFF:3 SECT:403 OBJ:407 RAND:Y

67. ANS:a TYPE:M DIFF:2 SECT:403 OBJ:408 RAND:Y

68. ANS:d TYPE:M DIFF:3 SECT:403 OBJ:408 RAND:Y

69. ANS:b TYPE:M DIFF:1 SECT:404 OBJ:409 RAND:Y

70. ANS:e TYPE:M DIFF:2 SECT:404 OBJ:410 RAND:Y

71. ANS:d TYPE:M DIFF:2 SECT:404 OBJ:409 RAND:Y

72. ANS:a TYPE:M DIFF:2 SECT:404 OBJ:411 RAND:Y

73. ANS:c TYPE:M DIFF:3 SECT:404 OBJ:411 RAND:Y

74. ANS:d TYPE:M DIFF:2 SECT:404 OBJ:412 RAND:Y

75. ANS:b TYPE:M DIFF:2 SECT:404 OBJ:412 RAND:Y

76. ANS:a TYPE:M DIFF:3 SECT:404 OBJ:412 RAND:Y

77. ANS:d TYPE:M DIFF:3 SECT:404 OBJ:412 RAND:Y

78. ANS:c TYPE:M DIFF:2 SECT:405 OBJ:413 RAND:Y

79. ANS:d TYPE:M DIFF:2 SECT:405 OBJ:414 RAND:Y

80. ANS:a TYPE:M DIFF:3 SECT:405 OBJ:414 RAND:Y

81. ANS:c TYPE:M DIFF:3 SECT:405 OBJ:414 RAND:Y

82. ANS:e TYPE:M DIFF:2 SECT:405 OBJ:415 RAND:Y

83. ANS:d TYPE:M DIFF:2 SECT:405 OBJ:415 RAND:Y

84. ANS:c TYPE:M DIFF:3 SECT:405 OBJ:415 RAND:Y

85. ANS:a TYPE:M DIFF:2 SECT:405 OBJ:415 RAND:Y

86. ANS:b TYPE:M DIFF:1 SECT:406 OBJ:416 RAND:Y

87. ANS:e TYPE:M DIFF:1 SECT:406 OBJ:416 RAND:Y

88. ANS:b TYPE:M DIFF:1 SECT:406 OBJ:416 RAND:Y

89. ANS:a TYPE:M DIFF:2 SECT:406 OBJ:416 RAND:Y

90. ANS:b TYPE:M DIFF:2 SECT:406 OBJ:416 RAND:Y

91. ANS:b TYPE:M DIFF:2 SECT:406 OBJ:416 RAND:Y

92. ANS:c TYPE:M DIFF:3 SECT:406 OBJ:416 RAND:Y

93. ANS:d TYPE:M DIFF:3 SECT:406 OBJ:416 RAND:Y

94. ANS:e   TYPE:M   DIFF:2   SECT:406   OBJ:417   RAND:Y

95. ANS:a   TYPE:M   DIFF:3   SECT:406   OBJ:417   RAND:Y

96. ANS:e   TYPE:M   DIFF:2   SECT:407   OBJ:418   RAND:Y

97. ANS:a   TYPE:M   DIFF:2   SECT:407   OBJ:418   RAND:Y

98. ANS:b   TYPE:M   DIFF:2   SECT:407   OBJ:418   RAND:Y

99. ANS:d   TYPE:M   DIFF:2   SECT:407   OBJ:419   RAND:Y

100. ANS:b   TYPE:M   DIFF:3   SECT:407   OBJ:419   RAND:Y

CHAPTER 5: RATIONAL EXPRESSIONS

SHORT ANSWER

1. Evaluate $\dfrac{5x - 8}{x + 4}$ for $x = 2$

2. Evaluate $\dfrac{9y - 1}{5 - 2y}$ for $y = 0$

3. Determine any values of the variable for which the rational expression is undefined:

$$\frac{6x}{5x - 8}$$

4. Determine any values of the variable for which the rational expression is undefined:

$$\frac{k + 8}{3k^2 + 4k - 4}$$

5. Write in lowest terms:

$$\frac{9a^4 b^6}{24a^8 b}$$

6. Write in lowest terms:

$$\frac{5y + 15}{8y + 24}$$

7. Write in lowest terms:

$$\frac{2x^2 - 7x - 72}{2x^2 - 18x + 16}$$

8. Write in lowest terms:

$$\frac{y - 2}{2 - y}$$

9. Write in lowest terms:

$$\frac{6 - x - x^2}{x^2 + 3x - 10}$$

10. Find the product (answer in lowest terms):

$$\frac{12x^2}{25y^3} \cdot \frac{10y^2}{9x^5}$$

11. Find the product (answer in lowest terms):

$$\frac{x^2 + 9x}{x^2 - 81} \cdot \frac{x^2 - 7x - 18}{x^3 + 2x^2}$$

12. Find the product (answer in lowest terms):

$$\frac{x^2 - 2xy - 3y^2}{x^2 - y^2} \cdot \frac{3x^2 - 2xy - y^2}{3x^2 + xy}$$

13. Find the quotient (answer in lowest terms):

$$\frac{x^2 - 3x - 10}{25 - x^2} \div \frac{x^2 + x - 2}{x^2 + 2x - 15}$$

14. Find the quotient (answer in lowest terms):

$$\frac{2x^2 + xy - 15y^2}{x^2 - 5xy - 24y^2} \div \frac{2x^2 + 7xy - 30y^2}{x^2 - 7xy - 8y^2}$$

15. Find the quotient (answer in lowest terms):

$$\frac{x^2 - 16}{8 - 2x - x^2} \div \frac{x^2 + 11x}{x^2 - 13x + 22}$$

16. Find the product (answer in lowest terms):

$$\frac{2y^2 - 8y + 6}{y^2 + 5y - 24} \cdot \frac{y^2 + 7y - 8}{2y + 10}$$

17. Find the least common denominator:

$$\frac{5}{4y^3} \text{ and } \frac{7}{6y^2}$$

18. Find the least common denominator:

$$\frac{m}{m^2 - 49} \text{ and } \frac{m + 2}{m^2 - 4m - 21}$$

19. Find the least common denominator:

$$\frac{t + 3}{t^2 + 4t + 4} \text{ and } \frac{t - 1}{t^2 + 2t}$$

20. Find the missing numerator:

$$\frac{5}{3x^4} = \frac{?}{18x^{12}}$$

21. Find the missing numerator:

$$\frac{5r}{r - 6} = \frac{?}{r^2 + 3r - 54}$$

22. Add (answer in lowest terms):

$$\frac{5x^2 + 3}{x^2 + 8} + \frac{9 - 2x^2}{x^2 + 8}$$

107

23. Perform the indicated operation (answer in lowest terms):

$$\frac{5y}{y^2 - 4} - \frac{10}{y^2 - 4}$$

24. Perform the indicated operation (answer in lowest terms):

$$\frac{3y^4 - 2}{y^3 + 5} - \frac{9 - y^4}{y^3 + 5}$$

25. Perform the indicated operation (answer in lowest terms):

$$\frac{3y}{9y^2 - 4} - \frac{2}{9y^2 - 4}$$

26. Perform the indicated operation (answer in lowest terms):

$$\frac{2x + 3}{x^2 - 16} - \frac{x + 1}{x - 4}$$

27. Perform the indicated operation (answer in lowest terms):

$$\frac{5x}{x^2 + x - 20} + \frac{2}{x^2 - 7x + 12}$$

28. Perform the indicated operation (answer in lowest terms):

$$\frac{x + 3}{x^2 + 8x} + \frac{x}{x^2 - 64}$$

29. Perform the indicated operation (answer in lowest terms):

$$\frac{x^2 + 51}{x^2 + 6x - 27} - \frac{x + 2}{x - 3}$$

30. Perform the indicated operation (answer in lowest terms):

$$\frac{x - 4}{x + 5} - \frac{x^2 + 11}{x^2 + 6x + 5}$$

31. Simplify (answer in lowest terms):

$$\frac{-\frac{4}{9}}{\frac{8}{3}}$$

32. Simplify (answer in lowest terms):

$$\frac{\frac{2a}{3b}}{\frac{6}{a}}$$

33. Simplify (answer in lowest terms):

$$\frac{\frac{5}{6} + \frac{3}{8}}{-\frac{2}{3} + \frac{5}{6}}$$

34. Simplify (answer in lowest terms):

$$\frac{\frac{5}{x} - \frac{3}{2x^2}}{9 - \frac{4}{x}}$$

35. Simplify (answer in lowest terms):

$$\frac{\frac{5}{y} - \frac{2}{y^2}}{\frac{5}{y^3} - \frac{2}{y^4}}$$

36. Simplify (answer in lowest terms):

$$\frac{\frac{3}{t + 2} - \frac{1}{t - 2}}{\frac{4}{t + 2} + \frac{5}{t - 2}}$$

37. Solve:

$$\frac{8x - 3}{2} + \frac{5x}{6} = \frac{10x + 1}{4}$$

38. Solve:

$$\frac{3}{2x} + \frac{5}{x + 1} = \frac{21}{4x}$$

39. Solve:

$$\frac{5}{x - 3} + \frac{2}{x} = 2$$

40. Solve:

$$\frac{3}{x} + \frac{2}{y} = \frac{4}{w} \text{ for } x$$

41. Solve:

$$z = \frac{3w}{t + 2} \text{ for } t$$

109

42. Solve for x:

$$\frac{5}{3x} = -\frac{2}{5}$$

43. Solve for y:

$$\frac{3y}{y + 5} = \frac{y + 4}{y + 1}$$

44. On a map, 4 inches represents 9 miles. How many miles does 7 inches represent?

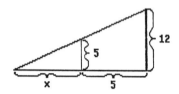

45. In the above triangle, find x

46. Pipe A, working alone, can fill a tank in 5 hours. Pipe B, working alone, can fill the same tank in 6 hours. How many hours would it take both pipes, working together, to fill that tank?

47. Rob walked 3 miles in the same amount of time that Lora biked 12 miles. If Lora's speed was 5 mph faster than Rob's speed, how fast was Rob walking?

48. Suppose t varies inversely as w and t = 3 when w = 12. Find t when w = $\frac{1}{4}$

49. Suppose x varies directly as the square of M and x = 24 when M = 4. Find x when M = $\frac{1}{2}$

50. The distance a ball rolls down an inclined plane varies directly as the square of the time elapsed. If the ball rolls 12 feet during the first half second, how far does it roll in 3 seconds?

MULTIPLE CHOICE

51. Evaluate $\dfrac{4y - 9}{y + 3}$ for $y = 3$

    a. -1

    b. $-\dfrac{5}{4}$

    c. $\dfrac{1}{2}$

    d. 1

    e. none of these

52. Evaluate $\dfrac{6t - 2}{7 - 5t}$ for $t = 0$

    a. $\dfrac{2}{5}$

    b. $-\dfrac{2}{7}$

    c. 2

    d. $-\dfrac{6}{5}$

    e. none of these

53. Determine any values of the variable for which the rational expression is undefined:

$$\dfrac{4x}{3x - 2}$$

    a. $x = 0$ or $x = \dfrac{2}{3}$

    b. $x = 0$ only

    c. $x = \dfrac{2}{3}$ only

    d. $x = -\dfrac{2}{3}$ only

    e. none of these

54. Determine any values of the variable for which the rational expression is undefined:

$$\frac{y + 5}{2y^2 + 3y - 27}$$

a. $y = -5$ only

b. $y = -5$ or $y = -\frac{9}{2}$ or $y = 3$

c. $y = \frac{9}{2}$ or $y = -3$ only

d. $y = -5$ or $y = \frac{9}{2}$ or $y = -3$

e. none of these

55. Write in lowest terms:

$$\frac{15x^6 y^{12}}{27x^2 y^{36}}$$

a. $\dfrac{5x^3}{9y^3}$

b. $\dfrac{5x^8}{9x^{48}}$

c. $\dfrac{5x^3}{9y^{24}}$

d. $\dfrac{5x^4}{9y^{24}}$

e. none of these

56. Write in lowest terms:

$$\frac{3y + 21}{2y + 14}$$

a. 3

b. $\dfrac{3}{2}$

c. $\dfrac{9}{4}$

d. 7

e. none of these

112

57. Write in lowest terms:

$$\frac{3x^2 + 13x - 10}{3x^2 + 9x - 30}$$

a. $\dfrac{3x - 2}{3(x - 2)}$

b. 1

c. $\dfrac{13}{9}$

d. $\dfrac{3x - 5}{x + 5}$

e. none of these

58. Write in lowest terms:

$$\frac{y - 11}{11 - y}$$

a. 1
b. −1
c. 2
d. −2
e. none of these

59. Write in lowest terms:

$$\frac{56 - x - x^2}{x^2 - x - 42}$$

a. $-\dfrac{4}{3}$

b. $-\dfrac{(x + 8)}{(x + 6)}$

c. $-\dfrac{(x - 8)}{(x + 6)}$

d. $-\dfrac{(8 - x)}{(x + 6)}$

e. none of these

60. Find the product (answer in lowest terms):

$$\frac{15x^3}{8y^{10}} \cdot \frac{12y^5}{35x}$$

a. $\frac{9x^3}{14y^2}$

b. $\frac{9x^2}{14y^2}$

c. $\frac{9x^2}{14y^{15}}$

d. $\frac{9x^2}{14y^5}$

e. none of these

61. Find the product (answer in lowest terms):

$$\frac{t^3 + 8t^2}{t^2 - 64} \cdot \frac{t^2 - 14t + 48}{t^2 - 6t}$$

a. t

b. $\frac{t^3 + 8t^2}{t^2 - 6t}$

c. $\frac{t(t + 6)}{t - 6}$

d. $\frac{t^3 + 8t^2}{t(t + 8)}$

e. none of these

62. Find the product (answer in lowest terms):

$$\frac{w^2 - 3mw - 10m^2}{w^2 - 4m^2} \cdot \frac{5w^2 - 9mw - 2m^2}{5w^2 + mw}$$

a. $1 - 5m$

b. $\frac{(w + 5m)(5w - m)}{w(5w + m)}$

c. $\frac{w - 5m}{w}$

d. $\frac{5w - m}{w}$

e. none of these

63. Find the quotient (answer in lowest terms):

$$\frac{x^2 + 9x - 36}{9 - x^2} \div \frac{x^2 + 14x + 24}{x^2 + x - 6}$$

a. -1

b. $\frac{x - 2}{x + 2}$

c. $\frac{x - 3}{x + 3}$

d. $\frac{2 - x}{x + 2}$

e. none of these

64. Find the quotient (answer in lowest terms):

$$\frac{3x^2 - xy - 10y^2}{x^2 + 7xy - 18y^2} \div \frac{3x^2 - 19xy - 40y^2}{x^2 + 2xy - 63y^2}$$

a. $\frac{(3x - 5y)(x - 7y)}{(3x + 5y)(x + 9y)}$

b. $\frac{x - 7y}{x - 8y}$

c. $\frac{x - 2y}{3x + 5y}$

d. $\frac{(x + 2y)(x - 7y)}{(x - 2y)(x + 8y)}$

e. none of these

65. Find the quotient (answer in lowest terms):

$$\frac{x^2 - 25}{55 - 6x - x^2} \div \frac{x^2 - 9x}{x^2 - 7x - 18}$$

a. $-\frac{(x + 5)(x + 2)}{x(x + 11)}$

b. $-\frac{(x + 5)(x + 2)}{x(11 - x)}$

c. $\frac{(x + 5)(x + 2)(x - 9)}{(x + 3)(x - 3)}$

d. $\frac{(x - 5)(x + 2)}{(11 + x)(x)}$

e. none of these

66. Find the product (answer in lowest terms):

$$\frac{5y^2 + 7y - 6}{y^2 - 8y - 20} \cdot \frac{y^2 + 10y}{15y - 9}$$

a. $\frac{(y - 2)(y)}{3(y + 2)}$

b. $\frac{y}{3}$

c. $\frac{(y + 10)(y)}{3(y - 10)}$

d. $\frac{(5y - 3)(y)}{15y - 9}$

e. none of these

67. Find the least common denominator:

$$\frac{11}{9x^4} \text{ and } \frac{5}{6x^5}$$

a. $54x^9$
b. $18x^9$
c. $54x^5$
d. $36x^5$
e. none of these

68. Find the least common denominator:

$$\frac{t}{t^2 - 25} \text{ and } \frac{t + 3}{t^2 - 4t - 5}$$

a. $t(t + 3)(t + 5)(t - 5)^2(t + 1)$
b. $(t + 5)(t + 1)(t - 5)^2$
c. $(t + 5)(t + 1)(t - 5)$
d. $t(t + 5)(t + 1)(t - 5)$
e. none of these

69. Find the least common denominator:

$$\frac{y + 5}{y^2 + 8y + 16} \text{ and } \frac{y - 1}{y^2 + 4y}$$

a. $(y + 4)^2(y)$
b. $(y + 4)^3(y)$
c. $(y + 4)(y)$
d. $(y + 5)(y - 1)(y + 4)^2(y)$
e. none of these

70. Find the missing numerator:

$$\frac{9}{5x^3} = \frac{?}{15x^9}$$

a. $3x^3$
b. $27x^3$
c. $3x^6$
d. $27x^6$
e. none of these

71. Find the missing numerator:

$$\frac{5y}{y - 8} = \frac{?}{y^2 - 4y - 32}$$

a. $5y(-3y + 4)$
b. $5y(y^2)$
c. $5y(y - 4)$
d. $5y(y - 8)$
e. none of these

72. Add (answer in lowest terms):

$$\frac{3t^2 + 5}{t^2 + 12} + \frac{11 - t^2}{t^2 + 12}$$

a. $\dfrac{19}{12}$

b. $\dfrac{4t^2 + 16}{t^2 + 12}$

c. $\dfrac{16 + 2t^2}{t^2 + 12}$

d. $\dfrac{3}{2}$

e. none of these

117

73. Perform the indicated operation (answer in lowest terms):

$$\frac{3x}{x^2 - 16} - \frac{12}{x^2 - 16}$$

a. $\dfrac{3x - 12}{x^2 - 16}$

b. $\dfrac{3}{x + 4}$

c. $\dfrac{3x - 12}{2x^2 - 32}$

d. $\dfrac{3x}{x - 4}$

e. none of these

74. Perform the indicated operation (answer in lowest terms):

$$\frac{5t^3 - 8}{t^2 + 2} - \frac{14 - 2t^3}{t^2 + 2}$$

a. $\dfrac{3t^3 - 22}{t^2 + 2}$

b. $\dfrac{3t^3 - 6}{t^2 + 2}$

c. $3t - 3$

d. $7t - 11$

e. none of these

75. Perform the indicated operation (answer in lowest terms):

$$\frac{5y}{25y^2 - 9} + \frac{3}{25y^2 - 9}$$

a. $\dfrac{1}{5y - 3}$

b. $\dfrac{1}{5y + 3}$

c. $\dfrac{5y + 3}{25y^2 - 9}$

d. $\dfrac{2}{25y^2 + 5y - 12}$

e. none of these

76. Perform the indicated operation (answer in lowest terms):

$$\frac{5x + 2}{x^2 - 9} - \frac{x + 2}{x - 3}$$

a. $\dfrac{10x + 8 - x^2}{x^2 - 9}$

b. $\dfrac{x^2 + 10x + 8}{x^2 - 9}$

c. $\dfrac{4x}{x^2 - 9}$

d. $\dfrac{-(x^2 + 4)}{x^2 - 9}$

e. none of these

77. Perform the indicated operation (answer in lowest terms):

$$\frac{3x}{x^2 + x - 42} + \frac{5}{x^2 + 9x + 14}$$

a. $\dfrac{3x + 5}{(x + 7)(x - 6)(x + 2)}$

b. $\dfrac{3x + 5}{(x + 7)^2 (x - 6)(x + 2)}$

c. $\dfrac{3x^2 + x - 30}{(x + 7)(x - 6)(x + 2)}$

d. $\dfrac{3x^2 + 11x - 30}{(x + 7)(x - 6)(x + 2)}$

e. none of these

78. Perform the indicated operation (answer in lowest terms):

$$\frac{x + 5}{x^2 + 9x} + \frac{x}{x^2 - 81}$$

a. $\dfrac{2x^2 - 4x - 45}{x(x + 9)(x - 9)}$

b. $\dfrac{2x + 6}{x(x + 9)(x - 9)}$

c. $\dfrac{x^3 + 10x^2 - 4x - 45}{(x^2 + 9x)(x + 9)(x - 9)}$

d. $\dfrac{x^2 - 3x - 45}{x(x + 9)^2 (x - 9)}$

e. none of these

119

79. Perform the indicated operation (answer in lowest terms):

$$\frac{x^2 - 23}{x^2 + x - 12} - \frac{x + 5}{x + 4}$$

a. $\dfrac{x^2 - x - 18}{(x + 4)(x - 3)}$

b. $\dfrac{x^2 - x - 28}{(x + 4)^2 (x - 3)}$

c. $\dfrac{-2}{x - 3}$

d. $\dfrac{2x - 38}{(x + 4)(x - 3)}$

e. none of these

80. Perform the indicated operation (answer in lowest terms):

$$\frac{x + 5}{x - 2} - \frac{x^2 - 32}{x^2 - 8x + 12}$$

a. $-\left(\dfrac{5}{x - 2}\right)$

b. $-\left(\dfrac{1}{x - 6}\right)$

c. $\dfrac{x - x^2 + 37}{(x - 2)^2 (x - 6)}$

d. $\left[\dfrac{x + 62}{(x - 2)(x - 6)}\right]$

e. none of these

81. Simplify (answer in lowest terms):

$$\frac{-\frac{10}{21}}{\frac{3}{14}}$$

a. $-\dfrac{10}{3}$

b. $-\dfrac{20}{9}$

c. $-\dfrac{5}{49}$

d. $-\dfrac{5}{14}$

e. none of these

82. Simplify (answer in lowest terms):

$$\frac{\dfrac{5x}{2y}}{\dfrac{10}{x}}$$

a. $\dfrac{x^2}{4y}$

b. $\dfrac{x}{2y}$

c. $\dfrac{25}{y}$

d. $\dfrac{25x^2}{y}$

e. none of these

83. Simplify (answer in lowest terms):

$$\frac{\dfrac{2}{9} + \dfrac{3}{4}}{-\dfrac{1}{6} + \dfrac{1}{2}}$$

a. $-\dfrac{1}{2}$

b. $-\dfrac{20}{13}$

c. $\dfrac{35}{12}$

d. $\dfrac{5}{3}$

e. none of these

121

84. Simplify (answer in lowest terms):

$$\dfrac{\dfrac{4}{y} - \dfrac{5}{3y^2}}{12 - \dfrac{2}{y}}$$

a. $-\dfrac{1}{20y}$

b. $\dfrac{12y - 5}{36y^2 - 6y}$

c. $\dfrac{12y - 5}{12y - 2}$

d. $-\dfrac{5}{9y^2}$

e. none of these

85. Simplify (answer in lowest terms):

$$\dfrac{1 - \dfrac{9}{x^2}}{1 + \dfrac{3}{x}}$$

a. $x - 3$

b. $\dfrac{x - 3}{x}$

c. $\dfrac{x - 3}{x^2}$

d. $\dfrac{x - 3}{x^3}$

e. none of these

86. Simplify (answer in lowest terms):

$$\dfrac{\dfrac{5}{w + 5} - \dfrac{1}{w - 5}}{\dfrac{10}{w + 5} - \dfrac{3}{w - 5}}$$

a. $\dfrac{4}{7}$

b. 0

c. $\dfrac{4w - 6}{7w - 13}$

d. $\dfrac{4w - 30}{7w - 65}$

e. none of these

122

87. Solve:

$$\frac{5c - 9}{4} + \frac{3c}{8} = \frac{2c + 1}{3}$$

a. $\frac{2}{11}$

b $\frac{5}{3}$

c. $\frac{62}{23}$

d. $\frac{51}{19}$

e. none of these

88. Solve:

$$\frac{5}{3y} + \frac{9}{y + 2} = \frac{5}{6y}$$

a. $\frac{-5}{52}$

b. $\frac{-10}{59}$

c. $\frac{30}{69}$

d. $\frac{5}{58}$

e. none of these

89. Solve:

$$\frac{3}{6 - y} - \frac{2}{y} = 1$$

a. $y = 3$ only
b. $y = -3$ only
c. $y = 3$ or $y = -4$
d. $y = -3$ or $y = -4$
e. none of these

90. Solve for T:

$$\frac{5}{w} + \frac{2}{T} = \frac{3}{x}$$

a. $\dfrac{2wx}{3w - 5x}$

b. $\dfrac{2wx - 5x}{3w}$

c. $\dfrac{5wx}{3w - 2x}$

d. $\dfrac{5wx - 2x}{3w}$

e. none of these

91. Solve for y:

$$x = \frac{5m}{y - 3}$$

a. $5m + 3$

b. $\dfrac{5m}{x - 3}$

c. $\dfrac{5m + 3x}{x}$

d. $\dfrac{5m}{-2x}$

e. none of these

92. Solve for x:

$$\frac{9}{5x} = -\frac{4}{9}$$

a. $-\dfrac{1}{20}$

b. $-\dfrac{4}{5}$

c. $-\dfrac{81}{20}$

d. $-\dfrac{5}{4}$

e. none of these

124

93. Solve for y:

$$\frac{2y}{y + 3} = \frac{y - 2}{y - 3}$$

   a. all the solutions are between -3 and 2
   b. all the solutions are between -1 and 4
   c. all the solutions are between 5 and 10
   d. all the solutions are between 0 and 8
   e. none of the above

94. On a map, 5 inches represents 7 miles. How many miles
    does 11 inches represent?

   a. 15.2 miles

   b. $17\frac{6}{7}$ miles

   c. 15.4 miles

   d. $17\frac{3}{5}$ miles

   e. none of these

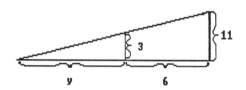

95. In the above triangle, find y

   a. $1\frac{7}{11}$

   b. $2\frac{1}{4}$

   c. $8\frac{1}{4}$

   d. $3\frac{2}{11}$

   e. none of these

96. A 3-inch diameter hose, working alone, can fill a spa in 7 hours, while a larger diameter hose, working alone, can fill the same spa in 5 hours. How many hours would it take both hoses, working together, to fill that spa?

    a. 2 hours and 11 minutes
    b. 2 hours and 55 minutes
    c. 3 hours and 5 minutes
    d. 3 hours and 26 minutes
    e. none of these

97. Suppose M varies inversely as t and M = 32 when t = 4. Find M when t = 5

    a. 1.6
    b. 40
    c. 25.6
    d. 30
    e. none of these

98. Jen jogged 2 miles in the same amount of time that Carl drove 20 miles. If Carl's speed was 30 mph faster than Jen's speed, how fast was Jen jogging?

    a. $2\frac{1}{4}$ mph

    b. $3\frac{1}{5}$ mph

    c. $2\frac{8}{11}$ mph

    d. $3\frac{1}{3}$ mph

    e. none of these

99. Suppose L varies directly as the square of y and L = 100 when y = 5. Find L when y = $\frac{2}{3}$

    a. $\frac{16}{9}$

    b. $\frac{80}{9}$

    c. $\frac{2,000}{9}$

    d. $\frac{10,000}{9}$

    e. none of these

100. The temperature at any point on a flat rectangular plate varies inversely as the square of the distance between the point and the heat source. If the temperature is 36° at a point which is 3 feet from the heat source, find the temperature at a point which is 2 feet from the heat source.

   a. 1°
   b. 16°
   c. 48°
   d. 81°
   e. none of these

1. TYPE:S DIFF:2 SECT:501 OBJ:501 RAND:Y

ANSWER:
$$\frac{1}{3}$$

2. TYPE:S DIFF:1 SECT:501 OBJ:501 RAND:Y

ANSWER:
$$-\frac{1}{5}$$

3. TYPE:S DIFF:2 SECT:501 OBJ:502 RAND:Y

ANSWER:
$$x = \frac{8}{5}$$

4. TYPE:S DIFF:3 SECT:501 OBJ:502 RAND:Y

ANSWER:
$$k = -2 \text{ or } k = \frac{2}{3}$$

5. TYPE:S DIFF:1 SECT:501 OBJ:503 RAND:Y

ANSWER:
$$\frac{3b^5}{8a^4}$$

6. TYPE:S DIFF:2 SECT:501 OBJ:503 RAND:Y

ANSWER:
$$\frac{5}{8}$$

7. TYPE:S DIFF:3 SECT:501 OBJ:503 RAND:Y

ANSWER:
$$\frac{2x + 9}{2(x - 1)} \text{ or } \frac{2x + 9}{2x - 2}$$

8. ANS:-1 TYPE:S DIFF:1 SECT:501 OBJ:504 RAND:Y

9. TYPE:S DIFF:2 SECT:501 OBJ:504 RAND:Y

ANSWER:

$$-\frac{(x + 3)}{(x + 5)}$$

10. TYPE:S DIFF:1 SECT:502 OBJ:505 RAND:Y

ANSWER:

$$\frac{8}{15x^3 y}$$

11. TYPE:S DIFF:2 SECT:502 OBJ:505 RAND:Y

ANSWER:

$$\frac{1}{x}$$

12. TYPE:S DIFF:3 SECT:502 OBJ:505 RAND:Y

ANSWER:

$$\frac{x - 3y}{x}$$

13. TYPE:S DIFF:2 SECT:502 OBJ:506 RAND:Y

ANSWER:

$$-\frac{(x - 3)}{(x - 1)}$$

14. TYPE:S DIFF:3 SECT:502 OBJ:506 RAND:Y

ANSWER:

$$\frac{x + y}{x + 6y}$$

15. TYPE:S DIFF:2 SECT:502 OBJ:506 RAND:Y

ANSWER:

$$\frac{(x - 4)(x - 11)}{x(x + 11)}$$

16. TYPE:S DIFF:2 SECT:502 OBJ:505 RAND:Y

ANSWER:
$$\frac{(y - 1)^2}{y + 5}$$

17. TYPE:S DIFF:1 SECT:503 OBJ:507 RAND:Y

ANSWER:
$12y^3$

18. TYPE:S DIFF:2 SECT:503 OBJ:507 RAND:Y

ANSWER:
$(m + 7)(m - 7)(m + 3)$

19. TYPE:S DIFF:2 SECT:503 OBJ:507 RAND:Y

ANSWER:
$t(t + 2)^2$

20. TYPE:S DIFF:1 SECT:503 OBJ:508 RAND:Y

ANSWER:
$30x^8$

21. ANS:$5r(r + 9)$ TYPE:S DIFF:2 SECT:503 OBJ:508 RAND:Y

22. TYPE:S DIFF:1 SECT:504 OBJ:509 RAND:Y

ANSWER:
$$\frac{3x^2 + 12}{x^2 + 8} \text{ or } \frac{3(x^2 + 4)}{x^2 + 8}$$

23. TYPE:S DIFF:2 SECT:504 OBJ:511 RAND:Y

ANSWER:
$$\frac{5}{y + 2}$$

24. TYPE:S DIFF:2 SECT:504 OBJ:509 RAND:Y

ANSWER:
$$\frac{4y^4 - 11}{y^3 + 5}$$

130

25. TYPE:S DIFF:2 SECT:504 OBJ:511 RAND:Y

ANSWER:
$$\frac{1}{3y + 2}$$

26. TYPE:S DIFF:2 SECT:504 OBJ:510 RAND:Y

ANSWER:
$$\frac{-x^2 - 3x - 1}{x^2 - 16}$$

27. TYPE:S DIFF:2 SECT:504 OBJ:510 RAND:Y

ANSWER:
$$\frac{5x^2 - 13x + 10}{(x + 5)(x - 4)(x - 3)}$$

28. TYPE:S DIFF:2 SECT:504 OBJ:510 RAND:Y

ANSWER:
$$\frac{2x^2 - 5x - 24}{x(x + 8)(x - 8)}$$

29. TYPE:S DIFF:3 SECT:504 OBJ:512 RAND:Y

ANSWER:
$$\frac{-11}{x + 9}$$

30. TYPE:S DIFF:3 SECT:504 OBJ:512 RAND:Y

ANSWER:
$$\frac{-3}{x + 1}$$

31. TYPE:S DIFF:1 SECT:505 OBJ:513 RAND:Y

ANSWER:
$$-\frac{1}{6}$$

32. TYPE:S DIFF:1 SECT:505 OBJ:513 RAND:Y

ANSWER:
$$\frac{a^2}{9b}$$

131

33. TYPE:S DIFF:2 SECT:505 OBJ:513 RAND:Y

ANSWER:
$$\frac{29}{4}$$

34. TYPE:S DIFF:2 SECT:505 OBJ:513 RAND:Y

ANSWER:
$$\frac{10x - 3}{18x^2 - 8x}$$

35. TYPE:S DIFF:3 SECT:505 OBJ:513 RAND:Y

ANSWER:
$$y^2$$

36. TYPE:S DIFF:3 SECT:505 OBJ:513 RAND:Y

ANSWER:
$$\frac{2t - 8}{9t + 2}$$

37. TYPE:S DIFF:1 SECT:506 OBJ:514 RAND:Y

ANSWER:
$$\frac{3}{4}$$

38. ANS:3 TYPE:S DIFF:2 SECT:506 OBJ:514 RAND:Y

39. TYPE:S DIFF:3 SECT:506 OBJ:514 RAND:Y

ANSWER:
$$x = \frac{1}{2} \text{ or } x = 6$$

40. TYPE:S DIFF:3 SECT:506 OBJ:515 RAND:Y

ANSWER:
$$x = \frac{3wy}{4y - 2w}$$

41. TYPE:S DIFF:2 SECT:506 OBJ:515 RAND:Y

ANSWER:
$$t = \frac{3w - 2z}{z}$$

42. TYPE:S DIFF:1 SECT:507 OBJ:516 RAND:Y

ANSWER:
$$-\frac{25}{6}$$

43. TYPE:S DIFF:2 SECT:507 OBJ:516 RAND:Y

ANSWER:
$$y = -2 \text{ or } y = 5$$

44. TYPE:S DIFF:2 SECT:507 OBJ:517 RAND:Y

ANSWER:
$$15\frac{3}{4} \text{ miles}$$

45. TYPE:S DIFF:2 SECT:507 OBJ:518 GRAPH FORMAT:G
QUESTION GRAPH:1 RAND:Y

ANSWER:
$$3\frac{4}{7}$$

46. TYPE:S DIFF:1 SECT:508 OBJ:519 RAND:Y

ANSWER:
$$2\frac{8}{11} \text{ hours}$$

47. TYPE:S DIFF:2 SECT:508 OBJ:519 RAND:Y

ANSWER:
$$1\frac{2}{3} \text{ mph}$$

48. ANS:144 TYPE:S DIFF:2 SECT:508 OBJ:520 RAND:Y

49. TYPE:S DIFF:2 SECT:508 OBJ:520 RAND:Y

ANSWER:

$$\frac{3}{8}$$

50. ANS:432 feet TYPE:S DIFF:3 SECT:508 OBJ:520 RAND:Y

51. ANS:c TYPE:M DIFF:2 SECT:501 OBJ:501 RAND:Y

52. ANS:b TYPE:M DIFF:1 SECT:501 OBJ:501 RAND:Y

53. ANS:c TYPE:M DIFF:2 SECT:501 OBJ:502 RAND:Y

54. ANS:e TYPE:M DIFF:3 SECT:501 OBJ:502 RAND:Y

55. ANS:d TYPE:M DIFF:1 SECT:501 OBJ:503 RAND:Y

56. ANS:b TYPE:M DIFF:2 SECT:501 OBJ:503 RAND:Y

57. ANS:a TYPE:M DIFF:3 SECT:501 OBJ:503 RAND:Y

58. ANS:b TYPE:M DIFF:1 SECT:501 OBJ:504 RAND:Y

59. ANS:b TYPE:M DIFF:2 SECT:501 OBJ:504 RAND:Y

60. ANS:d TYPE:M DIFF:1 SECT:502 OBJ:505 RAND:Y

61. ANS:a TYPE:M DIFF:2 SECT:502 OBJ:505 RAND:Y

62. ANS:c TYPE:M DIFF:3 SECT:502 OBJ:505 RAND:Y

63. ANS:d TYPE:M DIFF:2 SECT:502 OBJ:506 RAND:Y

64. ANS:b TYPE:M DIFF:3 SECT:502 OBJ:506 RAND:Y

65. ANS:a TYPE:M DIFF:2 SECT:502 OBJ:506 RAND:Y

134

```
66. ANS:c  TYPE:M  DIFF:2  SECT:502  OBJ:505  RAND:Y

67. ANS:e  TYPE:M  DIFF:1  SECT:503  OBJ:507  RAND:Y

68. ANS:c  TYPE:M  DIFF:2  SECT:503  OBJ:507  RAND:Y

69. ANS:a  TYPE:M  DIFF:2  SECT:503  OBJ:507  RAND:Y

70. ANS:d  TYPE:M  DIFF:1  SECT:503  OBJ:508  RAND:Y

71. ANS:e  TYPE:M  DIFF:2  SECT:503  OBJ:508  RAND:Y

72. ANS:c  TYPE:M  DIFF:1  SECT:504  OBJ:509  RAND:Y

73. ANS:b  TYPE:M  DIFF:2  SECT:504  OBJ:511  RAND:Y

74. ANS:e  TYPE:M  DIFF:2  SECT:504  OBJ:509  RAND:Y

75. ANS:a  TYPE:M  DIFF:2  SECT:504  OBJ:511  RAND:Y

76. ANS:d  TYPE:M  DIFF:2  SECT:504  OBJ:510  RAND:Y

77. ANS:d  TYPE:M  DIFF:2  SECT:504  OBJ:510  RAND:Y

78. ANS:a  TYPE:M  DIFF:2  SECT:504  OBJ:510  RAND:Y

79. ANS:c  TYPE:M  DIFF:3  SECT:504  OBJ:512  RAND:Y

80. ANS:b  TYPE:M  DIFF:3  SECT:504  OBJ:512  RAND:Y

81. ANS:b  TYPE:M  DIFF:1  SECT:505  OBJ:513  RAND:Y

82. ANS:a  TYPE:M  DIFF:1  SECT:505  OBJ:513  RAND:Y

83. ANS:c  TYPE:M  DIFF:2  SECT:505  OBJ:513  RAND:Y
```

84. ANS:b TYPE:M DIFF:2 SECT:505 OBJ:513 RAND:Y

85. ANS:b TYPE:M DIFF:3 SECT:505 OBJ:513 RAND:Y

86. ANS:d TYPE:M DIFF:3 SECT:505 OBJ:513 RAND:Y

87. ANS:c TYPE:M DIFF:1 SECT:506 OBJ:514 RAND:Y

88. ANS:b TYPE:M DIFF:2 SECT:506 OBJ:514 RAND:Y

89. ANS:e TYPE:M DIFF:3 SECT:506 OBJ:514 RAND:Y

90. ANS:a TYPE:M DIFF:3 SECT:506 OBJ:515 RAND:Y

91. ANS:c TYPE:M DIFF:2 SECT:506 OBJ:515 RAND:Y

92. ANS:c TYPE:M DIFF:1 SECT:507 OBJ:516 RAND:Y

93. ANS:d TYPE:M DIFF:2 SECT:507 OBJ:516 RAND:Y

94. ANS:c TYPE:M DIFF:2 SECT:507 OBJ:517 RAND:Y

95. ANS:b TYPE:M DIFF:2 SECT:507 OBJ:518 GRAPH FORMAT:G
    QUESTION GRAPH:2 RAND:Y

96. ANS:b TYPE:M DIFF:2 SECT:508 OBJ:519 RAND:Y

97. ANS:c TYPE:M DIFF:2 SECT:508 OBJ:520 RAND:Y

98. ANS:d TYPE:M DIFF:2 SECT:508 OBJ:519 RAND:Y

99. ANS:a TYPE:M DIFF:2 SECT:508 OBJ:520 RAND:Y

100. ANS:d TYPE:M DIFF:3 SECT:508 OBJ:520 RAND:Y

CHAPTER 6A: LINEAR EQUATIONS AND THEIR GRAPHS

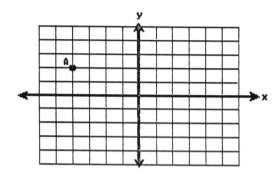

1. What are the coordinates of point A in the above diagram?

2. In which quadrant is (x,y) located if x is negative and y is positive?

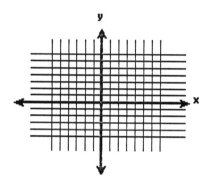

3. On the above diagram, plot (-1, -4)

4. Determine if (-1, 5) is a solution to x - 5y = 10

5. Find the ordered pair (x, y) that is a solution to 3x - 4y = 12 when y = 2

6. Find the ordered pair (x, y) that is a solution to 5x + 3y = 18 when x = 6

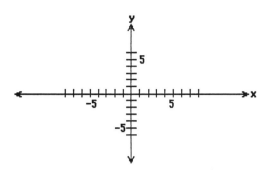

7. On the above coordinate plane, graph 2x + y = 6

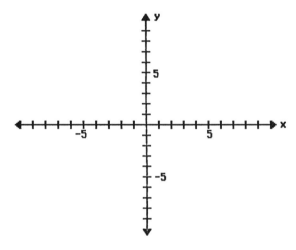

8. On the above coordinate plane, graph x = -4y + 3

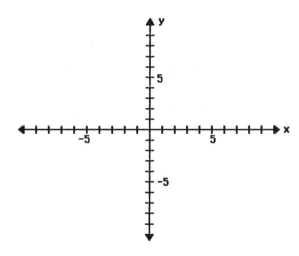

9. On the above coordinate plane, graph x = 3

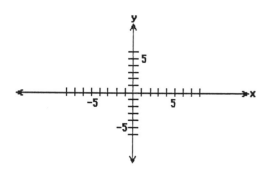

10. On the above coordinate plane, graph y = -2

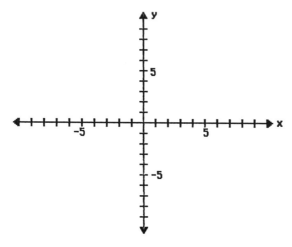

11. On the above coordinate plane, <u>use x and y intercepts</u> to graph
    3x - 2y = 12. (Label the x and y intercepts)

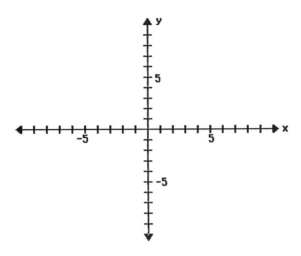

12. On the above coordinate plane, <u>use x and y intercepts</u> to graph 5x - 3y = 15. (Label the x and y intercepts)

13. Find the slope of the line passing through (-2, 4) and (6, -2)

14. Find the slope of the line passing through (7, -5) and (-2, 1)

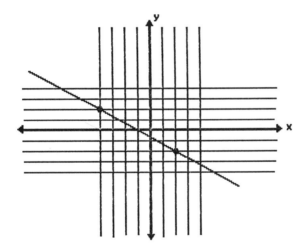

15. What is the slope of the line in the above diagram?

141

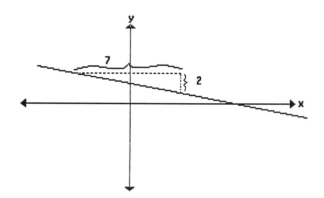

16. What is the slope of the line in the above diagram?

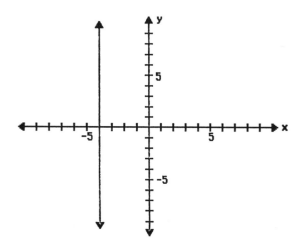

17. What is the slope of the line above?

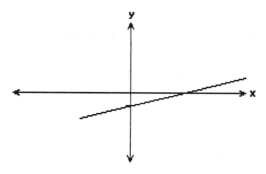

18. Does the line in the above diagram have a positive slope or a negative slope?

19. Is the line through (-5, 4) and (-1, 12) parallel to the line through (5, 8) and (6, 10)?

20. Are the following three points colinear? (-5, 1), (-1, 3), (2, 5)

21. Find the slope and y-intercept of 5x - 2y = 11

22. Find the slope and y-intercept of y = -3x + 8

23. Find an equation for the line whose slope is $\frac{5}{9}$ and whose y-intercept is -2

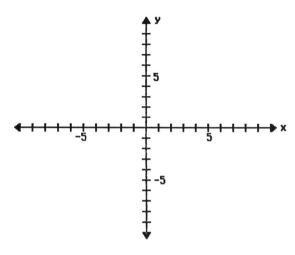

24. On the above coordinate plane, graph the line passing through (-2, 4) with a slope of -3

25. Find an equation for the line through (-4, 9) with a slope of -5. Answer in the form Ax + By = C

26. Find an equation for the line through (-8, 5) with a slope of $\frac{2}{3}$. Answer in the form Ax + By = C

27. Find an equation for the line through (-2, 9) and (3, -1). Answer in the form y = mx + b

28. Find an equation for the line through (3, -12) and (-4, 2). Answer in the form y = mx + b

29. Find an equation for the line with x-intercept 8 and y-intercept -3. Answer in the form y = mx + b

30. Find an equation for the line through (-2, 6) which is parallel to 5x + 8y = 11. Answer in the form Ax + By = C

143

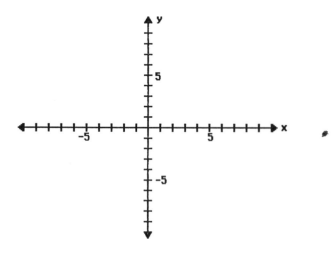

31. On the above coordinate plane, graph x - 4y > 8

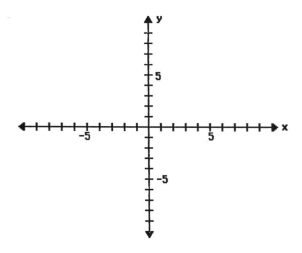

32. On the above coordinate plane, graph 2x - 3y ≤ 18

144

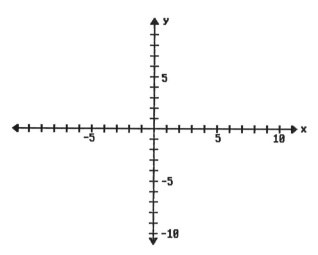

33. On the above coordinate plane, graph x < 3y

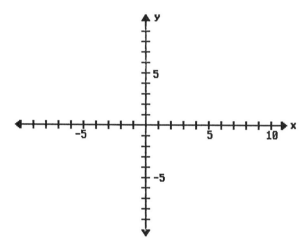

34. On the above coordinate plane, graph x ≤ -2

35. A company makes two types of radios, type A and type B. They make a profit of $80 on each radio of type A and a profit of $90 on each radio of type B. The combined profit from x radios of type A and y radios of type B must be at least $14,400. Express this restriction as a linear inequality.

36. A furniture company makes tables and chairs. Each table requires 5 hours in the finishing room and each chair takes 2 hours in the finishing room. They make x tables per week and y chairs per week. If the finishing room is available at most 70 hours per week, express this restriction as a linear inequality.

145

37. The price per radio is a function of the demand. When the number of radios in demand is 400, the price per radio is $32, while when the demand is 360, the price per radio is $34. Assume the price p per radio is linearly dependent upon the demand x. Write a linear equation that expresses p in terms of x.

38. The Acme Purse Company makes handbags with a fixed cost of $900 and a variable cost of $8 per handbag. If the company makes x handbags, express the total cost C in terms of x.

39. Is {(2, 5), (3, 9), (4, 9), (5, 10)} a function?

40. Is {(-5, 1), (-5, 3), (11, 4), (12, 5)} a function?

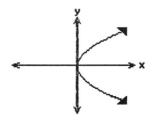

41. The graph of S is given above. Is S a function?

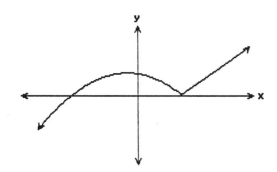

42. The graph of S is given above. Is S a function?

43. What is the domain of {(-3, 5), (6, 8), (9, 11)}?

44. What is the range of {(-9, 5), (-2, 6), (7, 15)}?

146

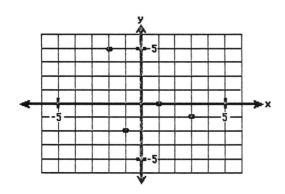

45. The graph of S is given by the 4 points shown above. What is the range of S?

46. What is the domain of $y = \dfrac{2}{x + 5}$?

47. What is the domain of $y = \dfrac{x + 3}{2x^2 - 9x + 10}$?

48. If $f(x) = 3x^2 + 2x - 1$, find $f(2)$

49. If $f(x) = 2x^2 - 9x + 3$, find $f(3)$

50. If $f(x) = 4x^2 - 3x + 8$, find $f(h)$

1. ANS:(-4, 2) TYPE:S DIFF:1 SECT:601 OBJ:601 GRAPH FORMAT:G
   QUESTION GRAPH:1 RAND:Y

2. TYPE:S DIFF:2 SECT:601 OBJ:602 RAND:Y

ANSWER:
     second quadrant

3. TYPE:S DIFF:1 SECT:601 OBJ:603 GRAPH FORMAT:G
   QUESTION GRAPH:2 ANSWER GRAPH:3 RAND:Y

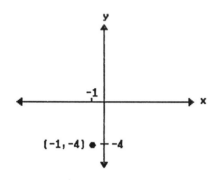

4. TYPE:S DIFF:1 SECT:602 OBJ:604 RAND:Y

ANSWER:
     not a solution

5. TYPE:S DIFF:2 SECT:602 OBJ:604 RAND:Y

ANSWER:
     $\left(\dfrac{20}{3},\ 2\right)$

6. ANS:(6, -4) TYPE:S DIFF:2 SECT:602 OBJ:604 RAND:Y

7. TYPE:**S** DIFF:**2** SECT:**602** OBJ:**605** GRAPH FORMAT:**G**
QUESTION GRAPH:**4** ANSWER GRAPH:**5** RAND:**Y**

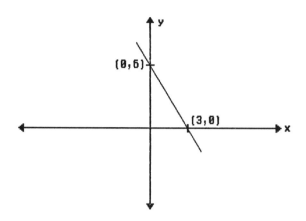

8. TYPE:**S** DIFF:**2** SECT:**602** OBJ:**605** GRAPH FORMAT:**G**
QUESTION GRAPH:**6** ANSWER GRAPH:**7** RAND:**Y**

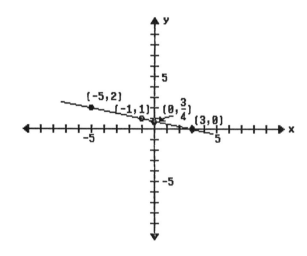

9. TYPE:**S** DIFF:**2** SECT:**602** OBJ:**607** GRAPH FORMAT:**G**
   QUESTION GRAPH:**8** ANSWER GRAPH:**9** RAND:**Y**

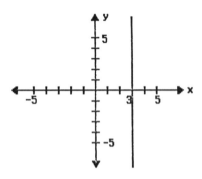

10. TYPE:**S** DIFF:**2** SECT:**602** OBJ:**607** GRAPH FORMAT:**G**
    QUESTION GRAPH:**10** ANSWER GRAPH:**11** RAND:**Y**

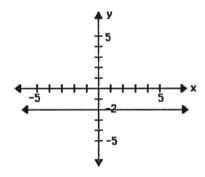

11. TYPE:**S** DIFF:**2** SECT:**602** OBJ:**606** GRAPH FORMAT:**G**
    QUESTION GRAPH:**12** ANSWER GRAPH:**13** RAND:**Y**

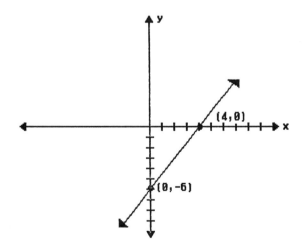

150

12. TYPE:S DIFF:2 SECT:602 OBJ:606 GRAPH FORMAT:G
    QUESTION GRAPH:14 ANSWER GRAPH:15 RAND:Y

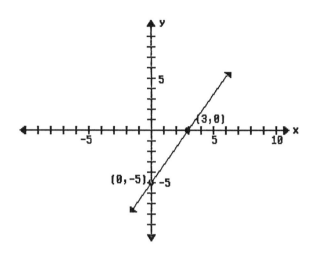

13. TYPE:S DIFF:2 SECT:603 OBJ:608 RAND:Y

ANSWER:
$$-\frac{3}{4}$$

14. TYPE:S DIFF:2 SECT:603 OBJ:608 RAND:Y

ANSWER:
$$-\frac{2}{3}$$

15. TYPE:S DIFF:2 SECT:603 OBJ:609 GRAPH FORMAT:G
    QUESTION GRAPH:16 RAND:Y

ANSWER:
$$-\frac{2}{3}$$

16. TYPE:S DIFF:3 SECT:603 OBJ:609 GRAPH FORMAT:G
    QUESTION GRAPH:17 RAND:Y

ANSWER:
$$-\frac{2}{7}$$

17. ANS:undefined TYPE:S DIFF:2 SECT:603 OBJ:610 GRAPH FORMAT:G
    QUESTION GRAPH:18 RAND:Y

151

18. TYPE:S DIFF:2 SECT:603 OBJ:611 GRAPH FORMAT:G
    QUESTION GRAPH:19 RAND:Y

ANSWER:
    positive slope

19. TYPE:S DIFF:2 SECT:603 OBJ:612 RAND:Y

ANSWER:
    yes, the lines are parallel

20. TYPE:S DIFF:2 SECT:603 OBJ:613 RAND:Y

ANSWER:
    no, they are not colinear

21. TYPE:S DIFF:2 SECT:604 OBJ:614 RAND:Y

ANSWER:
    slope = $\frac{5}{2}$, y-intercept = $-\frac{11}{2}$

22. TYPE:S DIFF:1 SECT:604 OBJ:614 RAND:Y

ANSWER:
    slope = -3, y-intercept = 8

23. TYPE:S DIFF:2 SECT:604 OBJ:615 RAND:Y

ANSWER:
    $y = \frac{5}{9}x - 2$

24. TYPE:S DIFF:2 SECT:604 OBJ:616 GRAPH FORMAT:G
    QUESTION GRAPH:20 ANSWER GRAPH:21 RAND:Y

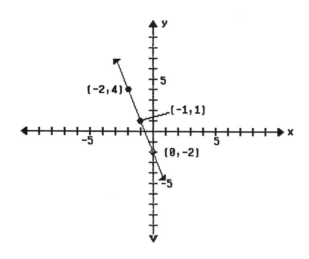

25. TYPE:S DIFF:2 SECT:604 OBJ:617 RAND:Y

ANSWER:
    $5x + y = -11$

26. TYPE:S DIFF:3 SECT:604 OBJ:617 RAND:Y

ANSWER:
    $2x - 3y = -31$

27. TYPE:S DIFF:2 SECT:604 OBJ:618 RAND:Y

ANSWER:
    $y = -2x + 5$

28. TYPE:S DIFF:2 SECT:604 OBJ:618 RAND:Y

ANSWER:
    $y = -2x - 6$

29. TYPE:S DIFF:3 SECT:604 OBJ:618 RAND:Y

ANSWER:
    $y = \frac{3}{8}x - 3$

30. TYPE:**S** DIFF:**2** SECT:**604** OBJ:**619** RAND:**Y**

ANSWER:
5x + 8y = 38

31. TYPE:**S** DIFF:**2** SECT:**605** OBJ:**620** GRAPH FORMAT:**G**
QUESTION GRAPH:**22** ANSWER GRAPH:**23** RAND:**Y**

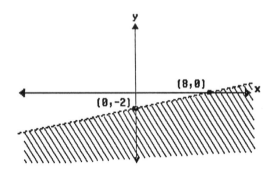

32. TYPE:**S** DIFF:**2** SECT:**605** OBJ:**620** GRAPH FORMAT:**G**
QUESTION GRAPH:**24** ANSWER GRAPH:**25** RAND:**Y**

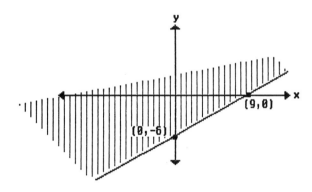

33. TYPE:**S** DIFF:**2** SECT:**605** OBJ:**620** GRAPH FORMAT:**G**
QUESTION GRAPH:**26** ANSWER GRAPH:**27** RAND:**Y**

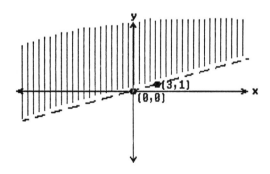

154

34. TYPE:S DIFF:1 SECT:605 OBJ:620 GRAPH FORMAT:G
QUESTION GRAPH:28 ANSWER GRAPH:29 RAND:Y

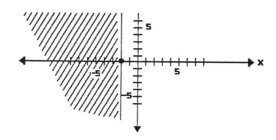

35. TYPE:S DIFF:2 SECT:605 OBJ:621 RAND:Y

ANSWER:
$80x + 90y \geq 14{,}400$

36. TYPE:S DIFF:2 SECT:605 OBJ:621 RAND:Y

ANSWER:
$5x + 2y \leq 70$

37. TYPE:S DIFF:2 SECT:606 OBJ:622 RAND:Y

ANSWER:
$p = -0.05x + 52$

38. TYPE:S DIFF:1 SECT:606 OBJ:622 RAND:Y

ANSWER:
$C = 8x + 900$

39. ANS:**yes** TYPE:S DIFF:2 SECT:607 OBJ:623 RAND:Y

40. ANS:**no** TYPE:S DIFF:2 SECT:607 OBJ:623 RAND:Y

41. ANS:**no** TYPE:S DIFF:2 SECT:607 OBJ:623 GRAPH FORMAT:G
QUESTION GRAPH:30 RAND:Y

42. ANS:**yes** TYPE:S DIFF:2 SECT:607 OBJ:623 GRAPH FORMAT:G
QUESTION GRAPH:31 RAND:Y

155

43. TYPE:**S** DIFF:**2** SECT:**607** OBJ:**624** RAND:**Y**

ANSWER:
$\{-3, 6, 9\}$

44. TYPE:**S** DIFF:**2** SECT:**607** OBJ:**624** RAND:**Y**

ANSWER:
$\{5, 6, 15\}$

45. TYPE:**S** DIFF:**2** SECT:**607** OBJ:**624** GRAPH FORMAT:**G**
QUESTION GRAPH:**32** RAND:**Y**

ANSWER:
$\{-2, -1, 0, 4\}$

46. TYPE:**S** DIFF:**2** SECT:**607** OBJ:**624** RAND:**Y**

ANSWER:
$\{x \mid x \neq -5\}$

47. TYPE:**S** DIFF:**3** SECT:**607** OBJ:**624** RAND:**Y**

ANSWER:
$\left\{x \mid x \neq 2 \text{ and } x \neq \frac{5}{2}\right\}$

48. ANS:**15** TYPE:**S** DIFF:**2** SECT:**607** OBJ:**625** RAND:**Y**

49. ANS:**-6** TYPE:**S** DIFF:**2** SECT:**607** OBJ:**625** RAND:**Y**

50. TYPE:**S** DIFF:**3** SECT:**607** OBJ:**625** RAND:**Y**

ANSWER:
$4h^2 - 3h + 8$

CHAPTER 6B: LINEAR EQUATIONS AND THEIR GRAPHS

MULTIPLE CHOICE

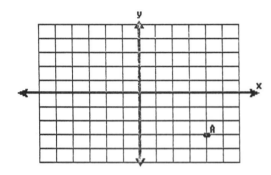

1. What are the coordinates of point A in the above diagram?

   a. (−3, 4)
   b. (4, −3)
   c. (3, −4)
   d. (−4, 3)
   e. none of these

2. In which quadrant is (x, y) located if x is positive and y is negative?

   a. I
   b. II
   c. III
   d. IV
   e. none of these

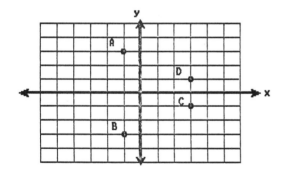

3. In the above diagram, which point has coordinates (−1, 3)?

   a. A
   b. B
   c. C
   d. D
   e. none of these

4. Which of the following is a solution to $3x - 2y = 12$

    a. $(4, -6)$
    b. $(4, 6)$
    c. $(2, -3)$
    d. $(0, 0)$
    e.   none of these

5. Find the ordered pair (x, y) that is a solution to $x - 5y = 15$ when $y = -2$

    a. $(25, -2)$

    b. $(5, -2)$

    c. $\left(-\frac{17}{5}, -2\right)$

    d. $\left(-\frac{13}{5}, -2\right)$

    e.   none of these

6. Find the ordered pair (x, y) that is a solution to $4x + 9y = 36$ when $x = 5$

    a. $\left(5, -\frac{9}{4}\right)$

    b. $\left(5, \frac{56}{9}\right)$

    c. $\left(5, \frac{16}{9}\right)$

    d. $\left(5, \frac{81}{4}\right)$

    e.   none of these

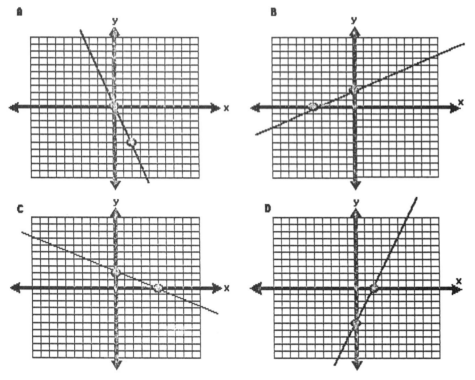

7. Which of the above is a graph of 5x - 2y = 10?

    a. A
    b. B
    c. C
    d. D
    e. none of these

A

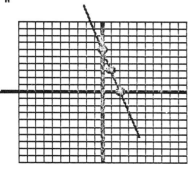

B

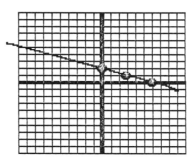

C

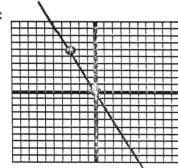

D

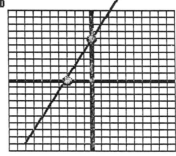

8. Which of the above is a graph of $x = -3y + 6$?

   a. A
   b. B
   c. C
   d. D
   e. none of these

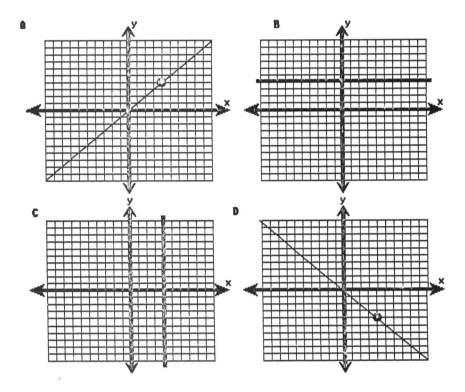

9. Which of the above is a graph of x = 4?

    a. A
    b. B
    c. C
    d. D
    e. none of these

10. Find the x-intercept for 5x + 3y = 15

    a. (5, 0)
    b. (0, 5)
    c. (3, 0)
    d. (0, 3)
    e. none of these

11. Find the y-intercept for 8x - 3y = 24

    a. (3, 0)
    b. (0, 3)
    c. (-8, 0)
    d. (0, -8)
    e. none of these

12. Find the x-intercept for $-3x + 5y = 16$

 a. $\left(0, -\frac{16}{3}\right)$

 b. $\left(-\frac{16}{3}, 0\right)$

 c. $\left(0, \frac{16}{5}\right)$

 d. $\left(\frac{16}{5}, 0\right)$

 e. none of these

13. Find the slope of the line passing through $(-5, 6)$ and $(-1, 8)$

 a. 2

 b. $\frac{1}{2}$

 c. -3

 d. $-\frac{1}{3}$

 e. none of these

14. Find the slope of the line passing through $(-3, 8)$ and $(-6, -2)$

 a. 2

 b. $-\frac{2}{3}$

 c. $-\frac{10}{9}$

 d. $\frac{3}{10}$

 e. none of these

1. ANS:**b** TYPE:**M** DIFF:**1** SECT:**601** OBJ:**601** GRAPH FORMAT:**G**
   QUESTION GRAPH:**1** RAND:**Y**

2. ANS:**d** TYPE:**M** DIFF:**2** SECT:**601** OBJ:**602** RAND:**Y**

3. ANS:**a** TYPE:**M** DIFF:**1** SECT:**601** OBJ:**603** GRAPH FORMAT:**G**
   QUESTION GRAPH:**2** RAND:**Y**

4. ANS:**c** TYPE:**M** DIFF:**1** SECT:**602** OBJ:**604** RAND:**Y**

5. ANS:**b** TYPE:**M** DIFF:**2** SECT:**602** OBJ:**604** RAND:**Y**

6. ANS:**c** TYPE:**M** DIFF:**2** SECT:**602** OBJ:**604** RAND:**Y**

7. ANS:**d** TYPE:**M** DIFF:**2** SECT:**602** OBJ:**605** GRAPH FORMAT:**G**
   QUESTION GRAPH:**3** RAND:**Y**

8. ANS:**b** TYPE:**M** DIFF:**2** SECT:**602** OBJ:**605** GRAPH FORMAT:**G**
   QUESTION GRAPH:**4** RAND:**Y**

9. ANS:**c** TYPE:**M** DIFF:**2** SECT:**602** OBJ:**607** GRAPH FORMAT:**G**
   QUESTION GRAPH:**5** RAND:**Y**

10. ANS:**c** TYPE:**M** DIFF:**2** SECT:**602** OBJ:**606** RAND:**Y**

11. ANS:**d** TYPE:**M** DIFF:**2** SECT:**602** OBJ:**606** RAND:**Y**

12. ANS:**b** TYPE:**M** DIFF:**2** SECT:**602** OBJ:**606** RAND:**Y**

13. ANS:**b** TYPE:**M** DIFF:**2** SECT:**603** OBJ:**608** RAND:**Y**

14. ANS:**e** TYPE:**M** DIFF:**2** SECT:**603** OBJ:**608** RAND:**Y**

CHAPTER 6C: LINEAR EQUATIONS AND THEIR GRAPHS

MULTIPLE CHOICE

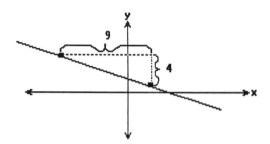

1. What is the slope of the line in the above diagram?

    a. $\frac{9}{4}$

    b. $\frac{4}{9}$

    c. $-\frac{9}{4}$

    d. $-\frac{4}{9}$

    e. none of these

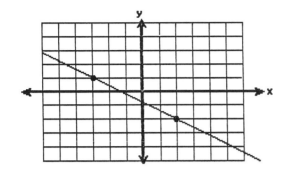

2. What is the slope of the line in the above diagram?

   a. $-\dfrac{5}{3}$

   b. $-\dfrac{3}{5}$

   c. $+\dfrac{5}{3}$

   d. $+\dfrac{3}{5}$

   e. none of these

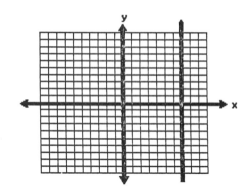

3. What is the slope of the line in the above diagram?

    a. 0

    b. 7

    c. undefined

    d. $\frac{1}{7}$

    e. none of these

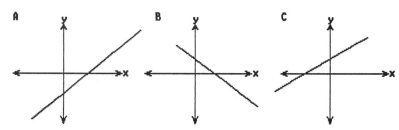

4. Which of the above lines has positive slope?

    a. both A and C
    b. both B and C
    c. A only
    d. B only
    e. C only

5. What is the slope of any line which is parallel to the line through (-5, 2) and (3, 9)?

    a. $-\dfrac{7}{2}$

    b. $\dfrac{7}{8}$

    c. $-\dfrac{8}{7}$

    d. $\dfrac{2}{7}$

    e.   none of these

6. Which of the following names three points which are colinear?

    a.   (-6, 4), (-4, 7), (-2, 11)
    b.   (-6, 4), (-4, 7), (-2, 10)
    c.   (-6, 4), (-4, 7), (-3, 11)
    d.   (-6, 4), (-4, 7), (-3, 10)
    e.   none of these

7. Find the slope of $3x + 5y = 28$

    a.   -3

    b. $\dfrac{28}{5}$

    c. $-\dfrac{3}{5}$

    d. $\dfrac{5}{3}$

    e.   none of these

8. Find the slope of $5x = 9y - 14$

a. $\frac{9}{5}$

b. $\frac{5}{9}$

c. $-\frac{14}{5}$

d. $-\frac{14}{9}$

e. none of these

9. Find an equation for the line whose slope is $\frac{8}{3}$ and whose y-intercept is -6

a. $y = -6x + \frac{8}{3}$

b. $y = 6x + \frac{8}{3}$

c. $y = \frac{8}{3}x + 6$

d. $y = \frac{8}{3}x - 6$

e. none of these

10. Find an equation for the line through $(-2, 11)$ with a slope of -3.

a. $4x + y = 3$
b. $-2x + 11y = -3$
c. $3x - y = 5$
d. $x + 3y = 31$
e. none of these

11. Find an equation for the line through $(-5, 6)$ whose slope is undefined.

a. $x = -5$
b. $x = 6$
c. $y = -5$
d. $y = 6$
e. none of these

170

12. Find an equation for the line through $(-3, 7)$ with a slope of $\frac{5}{6}$.

   a. $5x - 6y = 57$
   b. $6x - 5y = -53$
   c. $5x + 6y = 27$
   d. $6x + 5y = 17$
   e. none of these

13. Find an equation for the line through $(-6, 2)$ and $(-4, 10)$

   a. $y = 4x - 6$
   b. $y = -4x - 22$
   c. $y = 4x + 26$
   d. $y = -4x - 16$
   e. none of these

14. Find an equation for the line through $(5, -4)$ and $(3, 6)$

   a. $y = -5x + 21$

   b. $y = 5x - 21$

   c. $y = \frac{1}{5}x - 5$

   d. $y = -\frac{1}{5}x - 3$

   e. none of these

15. Find an equation for the line with x-intercept 4 and y-intercept -8.

   a. $y = -2x - 8$

   b. $y = 2x - 8$

   c. $y = \frac{1}{2}x - 8$

   d. $y = -\frac{1}{2}x - 8$

   e. none of these

16. Find an equation for the line through $(-5, 11)$ which is parallel to $2x - 9y = 4$.

   a. $2x + 9y = 89$
   b. $-2x + 9y = 109$
   c. $9x - 2y = -67$
   d. $9x + 2y = -23$
   e. none of these

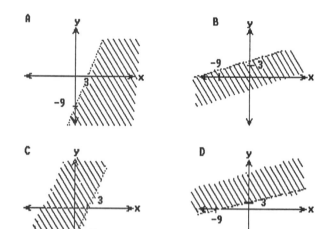

17. Which of the above is a graph of 3x - y > 9?

    a. A
    b. B
    c. C
    d. D
    e. none of these

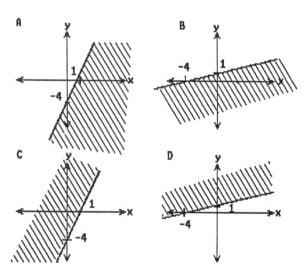

18. Which of the above is a graph of 4x - y ≤ 4?

    a. A
    b. B
    c. C
    d. D
    e. none of these

172

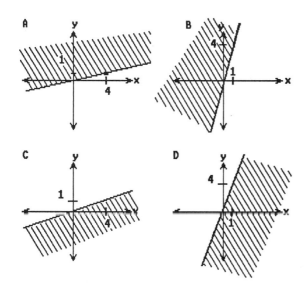

19. Which of the above is a graph of x < 4y?

    a. A
    b. B
    c. C
    d. D
    e. none of these

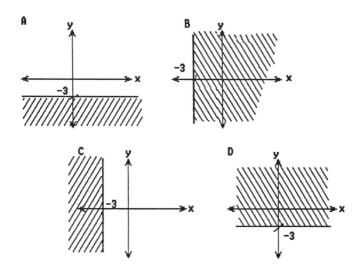

20. Which of the above is a graph of y ≥ -3?

    a. A
    b. B
    c. C
    d. D
    e. none of these

21. A company which makes pens and pencils makes a profit of $3 on each pen and a profit of $2 on each pencil. The combined profit from x pens and y pencils must be at least $4300. Express this restriction as a linear inequality.

    a. 3x + 2y ≥ 4300
    b. 3x + 2y ≤ 4300
    c. 2x + 3y ≥ 4300
    d. 2x + 3y ≤ 4300
    e. none of these

22. A company which makes plates and glasses knows that each plate costs them $4 to produce, while each glass costs them $3 to produce. The combined cost of x plates and y glasses must be less than $900. Express this restriction as a linear inequality.

    a. 3x + 4y > 900
    b. 3x + 4y < 900
    c. 4x + 3y > 900
    d. 4x + 3y < 900
    e. none of these

23. A manufacturing company makes necklaces with a fixed cost of $2300 and a variable cost of $29 per necklace. If the company makes x necklaces, express the total cost C in terms of x.

    a. C = 29x + 2300
    b. C = 29x - 2300
    c. C = 2300x + 29
    d. C = 2300x - 29
    e. none of these

24. When the number of vases demanded is 240, the price per vase is $44, while when only 232 vases are demanded, the price per vase is $48. Assume the price p per vase is linearly dependent upon the demand x. Write a linear equation that expresses p in terms of x.

    a. p = 0.5x + 76
    b. p = -0.5x + 164
    c. p = -2x + 524
    d. p = -2x + 328
    e. none of these

25. Which of the following is a function?

    a. {(2, 5), (2, 8), (3, 11), (4, 11)}
    b. {(-3, 9), (5, 9), (9, 6)}
    c. {(-4, 6), (7, 9), (7, 14)}
    d. {(-5, 1), (3, 2), (2, 8), (3, 14)}
    e. none of these

26. Which of the following is a function?

    a.   {(4, 9), (9, 3), (11, 3)}
    b.   {(-2, 8), (8, 5), (-2, 5)}
    c.   {(-3, 4), (4, 10), (4, 9)}
    d.   {(1, 5), (5, 6)), (6, 1), (1, 8)}
    e.   none of these

A
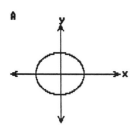

B
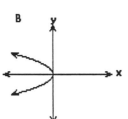

C
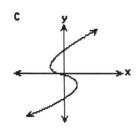

D
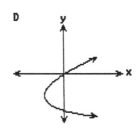

27. Which of the above is the graph of a function?

    a.   A
    b.   B
    c.   C
    d.   D
    e.   none of these

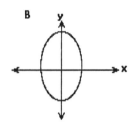

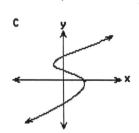

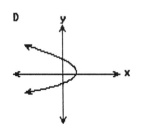

28. Which of the above is the graph of a function?

    a. A
    b. B
    c. C
    d. D
    e. none of these

29. What is the domain of {(2, 5), (8, 7), (3, 9), (5, 7)}?

    a. {2, 3, 5, 8}
    b. {5, 7, 9}
    c. {7, 15, 12}
    d. {2, 3, 5, 7, 8, 9}
    e. none of these

30. What is the range of {(-6, -2), (-3, 5), (9, 3), (4, 5)}?

    a. {-6, -3, 4, 9}
    b. {-2, 3, 5}
    c. {-8, 2, 9, 12}
    d. { -6, -3, -2, 3, 4, 5, 9}
    e. none of these

31. What is the range of {(-4, 5), (-2, 11), (14, -2)}?

    a. {-4, -2, 5, 11, 14}
    b. {1, 9, 12}
    c. {-4, -2, 14}
    d. {-2, 5, 11}
    e. none of these

32. What is the domain of $y = \dfrac{5}{x + 9}$?

    a.   all real numbers
    b. $\{x \mid x = -9\}$
    c. $\{x \mid x \neq -9\}$
    d. $\{x \mid x \neq -9 \text{ and } x \neq 5\}$
    e.   none of these

33. What is the domain of $y = \dfrac{5x + 2}{3x^2 - 2x - 5}$?

    a. $\{x \mid x \neq -\frac{2}{5} \text{ and } x \neq -\frac{5}{3} \text{ and } x \neq 1\}$

    b. $\{x \mid x \neq -\frac{2}{5} \text{ and } x \neq \frac{5}{3} \text{ and } x \neq -1\}$

    c. $\{x \mid x \neq -\frac{5}{3} \text{ and } x \neq 1\}$

    d. $\{x \mid x \neq \frac{5}{3} \text{ and } x \neq -1\}$

    e.   none of these

34. If $f(x) = 2x^2 + 5x - 4$, find $f(-1)$

    a. -11
    b.   3
    c. -1
    d. -5
    e.   none of these

35. If $f(x) = 5x^2 - 2x + 11$, find $f(3)$

    a.   230
    b.   50
    c.   35
    d.   20
    e.   none of these

36. If $f(x) = 3x^2 - 6x + 4$, find $f(t)$

    a. $t + 4$
    b. $-3t + 4$
    c. $3t^2 - 6t + 4$
    d. $t(3x^2 - 6x + 4)$
    e.   none of these

1. ANS:d TYPE:M DIFF:3 SECT:603 OBJ:609 GRAPH FORMAT:G
   QUESTION GRAPH:1 RAND:Y

2. ANS:b TYPE:M DIFF:2 SECT:603 OBJ:609 GRAPH FORMAT:G
   QUESTION GRAPH:2 RAND:Y

3. ANS:c TYPE:M DIFF:2 SECT:603 OBJ:610 GRAPH FORMAT:G
   QUESTION GRAPH:3 RAND:Y

4. ANS:a TYPE:M DIFF:2 SECT:603 OBJ:611 GRAPH FORMAT:G
   QUESTION GRAPH:4 RAND:Y

5. ANS:b TYPE:M DIFF:2 SECT:603 OBJ:612 RAND:Y

6. ANS:b TYPE:M DIFF:2 SECT:603 OBJ:613 RAND:Y

7. ANS:c TYPE:M DIFF:2 SECT:604 OBJ:614 RAND:Y

8. ANS:b TYPE:M DIFF:2 SECT:604 OBJ:614 RAND:Y

9. ANS:d TYPE:M DIFF:2 SECT:604 OBJ:615 RAND:Y

10. ANS:e TYPE:M DIFF:2 SECT:604 OBJ:617 RAND:Y

11. ANS:a TYPE:M DIFF:2 SECT:604 OBJ:617 RAND:Y

12. ANS:e TYPE:M DIFF:3 SECT:604 OBJ:617 RAND:Y

13. ANS:c TYPE:M DIFF:2 SECT:604 OBJ:618 RAND:Y

14. ANS:a TYPE:M DIFF:2 SECT:604 OBJ:618 RAND:Y

15. ANS:b TYPE:M DIFF:3 SECT:604 OBJ:618 RAND:Y

16. ANS:b TYPE:M DIFF:2 SECT:604 OBJ:619 RAND:Y

17. ANS:a TYPE:M DIFF:2 SECT:605 OBJ:620 GRAPH FORMAT:G
    QUESTION GRAPH:5 RAND:Y

18. ANS:c TYPE:M DIFF:2 SECT:605 OBJ:620 GRAPH FORMAT:G
    QUESTION GRAPH:6 RAND:Y

19. ANS:a TYPE:M DIFF:2 SECT:605 OBJ:620 GRAPH FORMAT:G
    QUESTION GRAPH:7 RAND:Y

20. ANS:d TYPE:M DIFF:1 SECT:605 OBJ:620 GRAPH FORMAT:G
    QUESTION GRAPH:8 RAND:Y

21. ANS:a TYPE:M DIFF:2 SECT:605 OBJ:621 RAND:Y

22. ANS:d TYPE:M DIFF:2 SECT:605 OBJ:621 RAND:Y

23. ANS:a TYPE:M DIFF:1 SECT:606 OBJ:622 RAND:Y

24. ANS:b TYPE:M DIFF:2 SECT:606 OBJ:622 RAND:Y

25. ANS:b TYPE:M DIFF:2 SECT:607 OBJ:623 RAND:Y

26. ANS:a TYPE:M DIFF:2 SECT:607 OBJ:623 RAND:Y

27. ANS:e TYPE:M DIFF:2 SECT:607 OBJ:623 GRAPH FORMAT:G
    QUESTION GRAPH:9 RAND:Y

28. ANS:a TYPE:M DIFF:2 SECT:607 OBJ:623 GRAPH FORMAT:G
    QUESTION GRAPH:10 RAND:Y

29. ANS:a TYPE:M DIFF:2 SECT:607 OBJ:624 RAND:Y

30. ANS:b TYPE:M DIFF:2 SECT:607 OBJ:624 RAND:Y

31. ANS:d TYPE:M DIFF:2 SECT:607 OBJ:624 RAND:Y

32. ANS:c TYPE:M DIFF:2 SECT:607 OBJ:624 RAND:Y

33. ANS:d TYPE:M DIFF:3 SECT:607 OBJ:624 RAND:Y

34. ANS:e TYPE:M DIFF:2 SECT:607 OBJ:625 RAND:Y

179

35. ANS:b TYPE:M DIFF:2 SECT:607 OBJ:625 RAND:Y

36. ANS:c TYPE:M DIFF:3 SECT:607 OBJ:625 RAND:Y

CHAPTER 7A: SYSTEMS OF EQUATIONS

SHORT ANSWER

1. Is (3, -2) a solution to the following system?

     5x + 4y = 7
     2x - y = 4

2. Is (-4, 5) a solution to the following system?

     2x + 5y = 17
     3x + 2y = 3

3. Is (9, -1) a solution to the following system?

     2x + 7y = 11
     3x - 2y = 29

4. How many solutions are there to an inconsistent system?

5. How many solutions are there to a dependent system?

6. Classify the following system as either dependent or inconsistent:

     y = -3x + 8
     y = -3x + 11

7. Classify the following system as either dependent or inconsistent:

     y = 5x - 3
     2y = 10x - 6

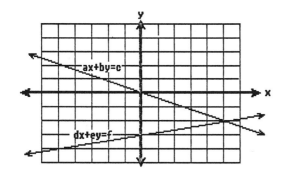

8. Use the above graph to determine the solution to:

     ax + by = c
     dx + ey = f

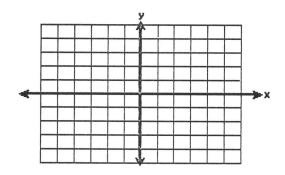

9. Use the above coordinate plane to solve by graphing:

$$x - 2y = 7$$
$$2x + y = 4$$

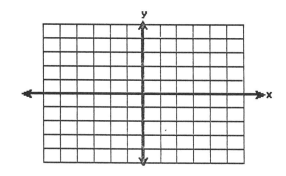

10. Use the above coordinate plane to solve by graphing:

$$x + 2y = 6$$
$$y = -2x$$

11. Solve by the <u>elimination method</u>:

$$x + 3y = 25$$
$$x - 3y = 7$$

12. Solve by the <u>elimination method</u>:

$$x + y = 14$$
$$-x + y = 8$$

13. Solve by the <u>elimination method</u>:

$$5w + t = -2$$
$$3w + 2t = 10$$

14. Solve by the _elimination method_:

$$x + 3y = -1$$
$$2x + 5y = -5$$

15. Solve by the _elimination method_:

$$2x - 3y = -2$$
$$3x + 4y = -20$$

16. Solve by the _elimination method_:

$$3x + 4y = -4$$
$$5x + 3y = -25$$

17. Solve by the _elimination method_:

$$5x - 2y = 3$$
$$-10x + 4y = 8$$

18. Solve by the _elimination method_:

$$3x - 5y = 11$$
$$9x - 15y = 21$$

19. Solve by the _elimination method_:

$$2x - 4y = 9$$
$$-x + 2y = 8$$

20. Solve by the _elimination method_:

$$5x - 10y = 45$$
$$2x - 4y = 18$$

21. Solve by the _elimination method_:

$$3x + 9y = 24$$
$$-2x - 6y = -16$$

22. Solve by the _elimination method_:

$$3x - y = 2$$
$$-6y + 2y = -4$$

23. Solve by the _elimination method_:

$$\frac{x}{5} + \frac{y}{3} = \frac{11}{15}$$

$$\frac{x}{2} - \frac{5}{4}y = 1$$

184

24. Solve by the <u>elimination method</u>:

$$-\frac{x}{2} + \frac{y}{3} = \frac{4}{3}$$

$$\frac{x}{5} + \frac{y}{3} = -\frac{1}{15}$$

25. Solve by the <u>substitution method</u>:

$$y = 3x$$
$$x + y = 12$$

26. Solve by the <u>substitution method</u>:

$$3x + 2y = 6$$
$$x = y - 8$$

27. Solve by the <u>substitution method</u>:

$$4a + 3b = 3$$
$$a + 2b = 7$$

28. Solve by the <u>substitution method</u>:

$$x + 5y = 18$$
$$2x - 9y = -2$$

29. Solve by the <u>substitution method</u>:

$$\frac{1}{2}x - \frac{2}{5}y = 6$$
$$x + y = 3$$

30. Solve by the <u>substitution method</u>:

$$\frac{2}{3}x - y = 12$$
$$x + 2y = -10$$

31. Solve by the <u>substitution method</u>:

$$3t - 5w = 10$$
$$w = \frac{3}{5}t - 2$$

32. Solve by the <u>substitution method</u>:

$$2m + 8y = 11$$
$$9 - m = 4y$$

185

33. Solve by the substitution method:

$$2a + 3b = 14$$
$$a = 2 - 1.5b$$

34. Solve by the substitution method:

$$4x + y = 12$$
$$x = 3 - 0.25y$$

35. The sum of two numbers is $\frac{5}{6}$. The difference of twice one number and three times the other number is -4. Write a system of equations you could use to find the two numbers (do not solve).

36. The length of a rectangle is 5 cm less than four times its width. The perimeter of the rectangle is 38 cm. Write a system of equations you could use to find the length and width of the rectangle (do not solve).

37. The sum of two numbers is 7. The difference of one number and twice the other number is 16. Find the two numbers.

38. The length of a rectangle is 3 inches less than twice its width. If the perimeter is 42 inches, find the dimensions of the rectangle.

39. A prescription calls for a cough syrup to have 3% codeine sulfate. The pharmacist has only cough syrup with 1% and another with 3.5% codeine sulfate. How many milliliters of each kind of cough syrup should be mixed to obtain 500ml of cough syrup with 3% codeine sulfate?

40. Solution A is 56% peroxide while solution B is 9% peroxide. How many liters of each solution should be mixed to obtain 1000 liters of a solution which is 18.4% peroxide?

41. A boat can travel 36 miles downstream in 2 hours and 30 miles upstream in 3 hours. Find the rate of the boat in still water.

42. A boat can travel 60 miles downstream in 3 hours and 75 miles upstream in 5 hours. Find the speed of the stream.

43. A company makes and sells x toasters each week with a total weekly cost C, in dollars, given by C = 8x + 3000. The toasters are sold for $14 each. Find the break-even level of production.

44. A company makes and sells x belts each week with a total weekly cost C, in dollars, given by C = 3x + 290. The belts are sold for $8 each. Find the break-even level of production.

186

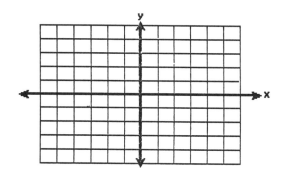

45. On the above coordinate plane, graph this system:

   2x + y < 6
   3x - 2y > 6

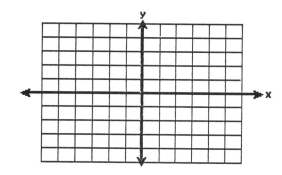

46. On the above coordinate plane, graph this system:

   3x - 4y < 12
    x + 2y > 4

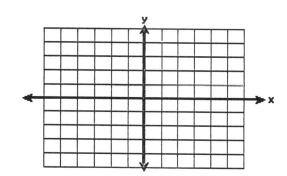

47. On the above coordinate plane, graph this system:

   x ≤ -3
   y ≥ 2

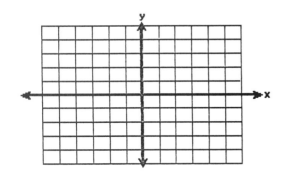

48. On the above coordinate plane, graph this system:

$$4x + 5y \leq 20$$
$$x \geq 0$$
$$y \geq 0$$

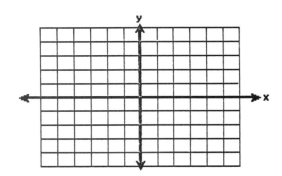

49. On the above coordinate plane, graph this system:

$$-2x + 6y \leq 12$$
$$x + y \leq 4$$

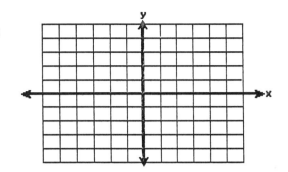

50. On the above coordinate plane, graph this system:

$$2x + 3y \geq 6$$
$$3x - y \leq 3$$
$$x \geq 0$$

1. ANS:no   TYPE:S   DIFF:1   SECT:701   OBJ:701   RAND:Y

2. ANS:no   TYPE:S   DIFF:1   SECT:701   OBJ:701   RAND:Y

3. ANS:yes   TYPE:S   DIFF:1   SECT:701   OBJ:701   RAND:Y

4. TYPE:S   DIFF:1   SECT:701   OBJ:702   RAND:Y

ANSWER:
     no solutions

5. TYPE:S   DIFF:1   SECT:701   OBJ:703   RAND:Y

ANSWER:
     infinitely many solutions

6. TYPE:S   DIFF:2   SECT:701   OBJ:702   RAND:Y

ANSWER:
     inconsistent

7. ANS:dependent   TYPE:S   DIFF:2   SECT:701   OBJ:703   RAND:Y

8. ANS:(5, -2)   TYPE:S   DIFF:3   SECT:701   OBJ:704   GRAPH FORMAT:G
   QUESTION GRAPH:1   RAND:Y

9. ANS:(3, -2)   TYPE:S   DIFF:2   SECT:701   OBJ:704   GRAPH FORMAT:G
   QUESTION GRAPH:2   ANSWER GRAPH:3   RAND:Y

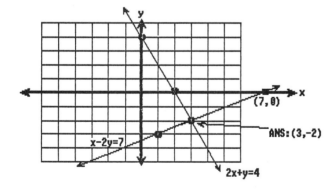

190

10. ANS:(−2, 4) TYPE:S DIFF:2 SECT:701 OBJ:704 GRAPH FORMAT:G
    QUESTION GRAPH:4 ANSWER GRAPH:5 RAND:Y

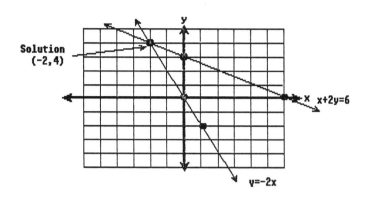

11. ANS:(16, 3) TYPE:S DIFF:1 SECT:702 OBJ:705 RAND:Y

12. ANS:(3, 11) TYPE:S DIFF:1 SECT:702 OBJ:705 RAND:Y

13. ANS:(−2, 8) TYPE:S DIFF:2 SECT:702 OBJ:705 RAND:Y

14. ANS:(−10, 3) TYPE:S DIFF:2 SECT:702 OBJ:705 RAND:Y

15. ANS:(−4, −2) TYPE:S DIFF:3 SECT:702 OBJ:705 RAND:Y

16. ANS:(−8, 5) TYPE:S DIFF:3 SECT:702 OBJ:705 RAND:Y

17. TYPE:S DIFF:2 SECT:702 OBJ:706 RAND:Y

ANSWER:
    no solution; system is inconsistent

18. TYPE:S DIFF:2 SECT:702 OBJ:706 RAND:Y

ANSWER:
    no solution; system is inconsistent

19. TYPE:S DIFF:2 SECT:702 OBJ:706 RAND:Y

ANSWER:
    no solution; system is inconsistent

191

20. TYPE:S DIFF:2 SECT:702 OBJ:707 RAND:Y

ANSWER:
    infinitely many solutions; the system is dependent

21. TYPE:S DIFF:2 SECT:702 OBJ:707 RAND:Y

ANSWER:
    infinitely many solutions; the system is dependent

22. TYPE:S DIFF:2 SECT:702 OBJ:707 RAND:Y

ANSWER:
    infinitely many solutions; the system is dependent

23. TYPE:S DIFF:3 SECT:702 OBJ:705 RAND:Y

ANSWER:
    $\left[3, \frac{2}{5} \right]$

24. ANS:(-2, 1) TYPE:S DIFF:3 SECT:702 OBJ:705 RAND:Y

25. ANS:(3, 9) TYPE:S DIFF:1 SECT:703 OBJ:708 RAND:Y

26. ANS:(-2, 6) TYPE:S DIFF:1 SECT:703 OBJ:708 RAND:Y

27. ANS:(-3, 5) TYPE:S DIFF:2 SECT:703 OBJ:708 RAND:Y

28. ANS:(8, 2) TYPE:S DIFF:2 SECT:703 OBJ:708 RAND:Y

29. ANS:(8, -5) TYPE:S DIFF:3 SECT:703 OBJ:708 RAND:Y

30. ANS:(6, -8) TYPE:S DIFF:3 SECT:703 OBJ:708 RAND:Y

31. TYPE:S DIFF:2 SECT:703 OBJ:710 RAND:Y

ANSWER:
    infinitely many solutions; the system is dependent

32. TYPE:S DIFF:2 SECT:703 OBJ:709 RAND:Y

ANSWER:
    no solution; the system is inconsistent

33. TYPE:S DIFF:2 SECT:703 OBJ:709 RAND:Y

ANSWER:
    no solution; the system is inconsistent

34. TYPE:S DIFF:2 SECT:703 OBJ:710 RAND:Y

ANSWER:
    infinitely many solutions; the system is dependent

35. TYPE:S DIFF:2 SECT:704 OBJ:711 RAND:Y

ANSWER:
$$x + y = \frac{5}{6}$$
$$2x - 3y = -4$$

36. TYPE:S DIFF:2 SECT:704 OBJ:711 RAND:Y

ANSWER:
$$l = 4w - 5$$
$$2l + 2w = 38$$

37. ANS:10 and -3 TYPE:S DIFF:1 SECT:704 OBJ:712 RAND:Y

38. TYPE:S DIFF:2 SECT:704 OBJ:712 RAND:Y

ANSWER:
    length = 13 inches; width = 8 inches

39. TYPE:S DIFF:2 SECT:704 OBJ:713 RAND:Y

ANSWER:
    100ml of the 1% cough syrup, 400ml of the 3.5% cough syrup

40. TYPE:S DIFF:2 SECT:704 OBJ:713 RAND:Y

ANSWER:
    800 liters of the 9% solution, 200 liters of the 56% solution

41. ANS:14 mph   TYPE:S   DIFF:2   SECT:704   OBJ:714   RAND:Y

42. ANS:2.5 mph   TYPE:S   DIFF:2   SECT:704   OBJ:714   RAND:Y

43. TYPE:S   DIFF:2   SECT:704   OBJ:715   RAND:Y

ANSWER:
    500 toasters per week

44. TYPE:S   DIFF:2   SECT:704   OBJ:715   RAND:Y

ANSWER:
    58 belts per week

45. TYPE:S   DIFF:2   SECT:705   OBJ:716   GRAPH FORMAT:G
    QUESTION GRAPH:6   ANSWER GRAPH:7   RAND:Y

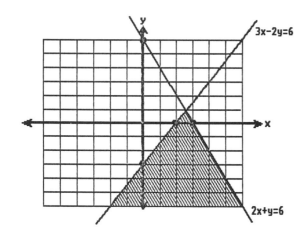

46. TYPE:S   DIFF:2   SECT:705   OBJ:716   GRAPH FORMAT:G
    QUESTION GRAPH:8   ANSWER GRAPH:9   RAND:Y

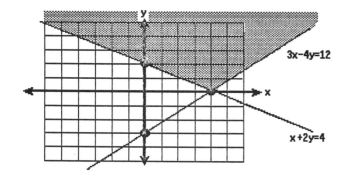

47. TYPE:**S** DIFF:**1** SECT:**705** OBJ:**716** GRAPH FORMAT:**G**
QUESTION GRAPH:**10** ANSWER GRAPH:**11** RAND:**Y**

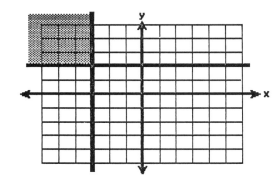

48. TYPE:**S** DIFF:**2** SECT:**705** OBJ:**716** GRAPH FORMAT:**G**
QUESTION GRAPH:**12** ANSWER GRAPH:**13** RAND:**Y**

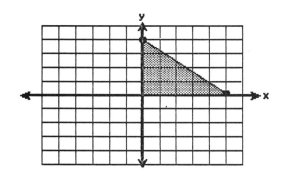

49. TYPE:**S** DIFF:**2** SECT:**705** OBJ:**716** GRAPH FORMAT:**G**
QUESTION GRAPH:**14** ANSWER GRAPH:**15** RAND:**Y**

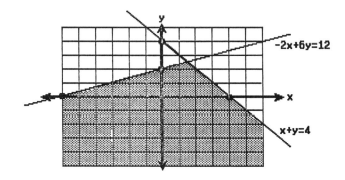

195

50. TYPE:S DIFF:3 SECT:705 OBJ:716 GRAPH FORMAT:G
    QUESTION GRAPH:16 ANSWER GRAPH:17 RAND:Y

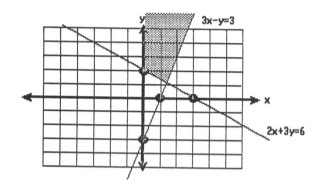

196

CHAPTER 7B: SYSTEMS OF EQUATIONS

MULTIPLE CHOICE

1. Which of the following is a solution to the system?

   $$2x - 9y = 17$$
   $$3x + 2y = 10$$

   a. (-5, -3)
   b. (0, 5)
   c. (13, 1)
   d. (4, -1)
   e. none of these

2. Which of the following is a solution to the system?

   $$4x - 3y = 1$$
   $$3x - 5y = 9$$

   a. (1, 1)
   b. (3, 0)
   c. (-2, -3)
   d. (-1, -9)
   e. none of these

3. Which of the following is a solution to the system?

   $$5x + 9y = 3$$
   $$3x + 5y = 1$$

   a. $(0, \frac{1}{3})$
   b. (6, -3)
   c. (-3, 2)
   d. $(\frac{1}{3}, 0)$
   e. none of these

4. How many solutions are there to an inconsistent system?

   a. 0
   b. 1
   c. 2
   d. infinitely many
   e. none of these

5. How many solutions are there to a dependent system?

   a. 0
   b. 1
   c. 2
   d. infinitely many
   e. none of these

6. Which of the following is true about this system?

$$y = -2x + 5$$
$$y = -2x + 4$$

a. The system has one unique solution and it is (5, 4)
b. The system has one unique solution and it is (0, 5)
c. The system is inconsistent
d. The system is dependent
e. none of these

7. Which of the following systems is dependent?

a. $y = 4x - 3$
     $5y = 20x - 1$

b. $y = 3x - 9$
     $y = 2x - 9$

c. $y = 2x + 3$
     $2y = 4x + 6$

d. $y = 6x - 1$
     $y = 12x - 2$

e. none of these

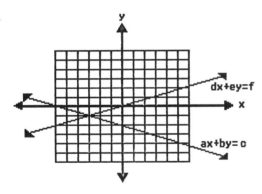

8. Use the above graph to determine the solution to:

$$ax + by = c$$
$$dx + ey = f$$

a. (-6, -2)
b. (-3, -1)
c. (0, 0)
d. (-6, 0)
e. none of these

199

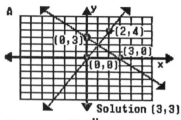

A Solution (3,3)

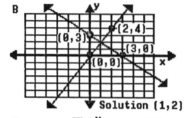

B Solution (1,2)

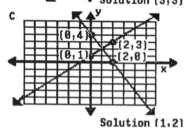

C Solution (1,2)

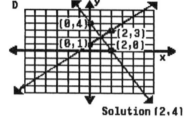

D Solution (2,4)

9. Which of the above is a solution to:

"Solve by graphing $\begin{cases} 2x + y = 4 \\ y = x + 1 \end{cases}$"?

a. A
b. B
c. C
d. D
e. none of these

200

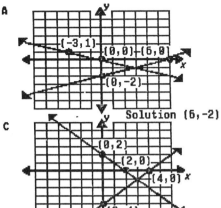

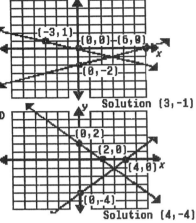

10. Which of the above is a solution to:

    "Solve by graphing $\begin{cases} x + 3y = 0 \\ x - 3y = 6 \end{cases}$"?

    a. A
    b. B
    c. C
    d. D
    e. none of these

11. Solve by the elimination method to find the x-coordinate of the solution:

    $$x + 5y = 8$$
    $$x - 5y = 12$$

    a. x = 10
    b. x = 20
    c. x = 8
    d. x = 12
    e. none of these

12. Solve by the elimination method to find the y-coordinate of the solution:

    $$3x + y = 11$$
    $$-3x + 2y = 1$$

    a. y = 11
    b. y = $\frac{1}{2}$
    c. y = 4
    d. y = 12
    e. none of these

13. Solve by the <u>elimination method</u> to find the y-coordinate of the solution:

$$2y + t = -4$$
$$5y + 3t = 7$$

a. $y = -2$
b. $y = \frac{3}{7}$
c. $y = -19$
d. $y = -\frac{5}{11}$
e. none of these

14. Solve by the <u>elimination method</u> to find the w-coordinate of the solution:

$$5m + 4w = 3$$
$$m + 3w = 16$$

a. $w = 7$
b. $w = \frac{19}{7}$
c. $w = 19$
d. $w = \frac{83}{11}$
e. none of these

15. Solve by the <u>elimination method</u> to find the x-coordinate of the solution:

$$4x + 3y = 22$$
$$3x - 2y = -26$$

a. $x = -4$
b. $x = -2$
c. $x = -\frac{4}{17}$
d. $x = -\frac{2}{17}$
e. none of these

16. Solve by the <u>elimination method</u> to find the r-coordinate of the solution:

$$2b + 5r = 11$$
$$3b - 2r = 26$$

a. $r = 37$
b. $r = \frac{37}{5}$
c. $r = 15$
d. $r = 2$
e. none of these

17. Solve by the elimination method:

$$2x + 7y = 9$$
$$5x - 3y = 4$$

a. The system is dependent
b. The system is inconsistent
c. The system has one unique solution and that solution is
   $\left\{\dfrac{13}{7}, \dfrac{13}{4}\right\}$
d. The system has one unique solution and that solution is
   $\left(\dfrac{55}{41}, \dfrac{37}{41}\right)$
e. none of these

18. Solve by the elimination method:

$$4x - 3y = 5$$
$$-8x + 6y = 11$$

a. The system is dependent
b. The system is inconsistent
c. The system has one unique solution and that solution is $(0, 16)$
d. The system has one unique solution and that solution is
   $\left(1, \dfrac{4}{3}\right)$
e. none of these

19. Solve by the elimination method:

$$3x - 2y = 5$$
$$9x - 6y = 2$$

a. The system has one unique solution and that solution is $(3, 2)$
b. The system has one unique solution and that solution is
   $\left(0, -\dfrac{5}{2}\right)$
c. The system is dependent
d. The system is inconsistent
e. none of these

20. Solve by the elimination method:

$$3x - 6y = 24$$
$$2x - 4y = 16$$

a. The system has one unique solution and that solution is $(8, -4)$
b. The system has one unique solution and that solution is $(0, 5)$
c. The system is dependent
d. The system is inconsistent
e. none of these

203

21. Solve by the elimination method:

$$5x + 10y = 35$$
$$3x + 6y = 21$$

   a. The system is dependent
   b. The system is inconsistent
   c. The system has one unique solution and that solution is
      $(7, \frac{7}{2})$
   d. The system has one unique solution and that solution is $(1, 2)$.
   e. none of these

22. Solve by the elimination method:

$$4x + 6y = 18$$
$$6x + 9y = 27$$

   a. The system has one unique solution and that solution is
      $(\frac{9}{2}, 3)$
   b. The system is dependent.
   c. The system has one unique solution and that solution is $(2, 3)$.
   d. The system is inconsistent.
   e. none of these

23. Solve by the elimination method:

$$\begin{cases} \dfrac{x}{2} + \dfrac{3y}{4} = 1 \\ \dfrac{3x}{8} + \dfrac{y}{2} = \dfrac{7}{8} \end{cases}$$

   a. The system is dependent
   b. The system is inconsistent
   c. The system has one unique solution and that solution is
      $(\frac{1}{2}, \frac{3}{8})$
   d. The system has one unique solution and that solution is $(5, -2)$
   e. none of these

24. Solve by the elimination method:

$$\begin{cases} \dfrac{x}{6} + \dfrac{y}{2} = \dfrac{-5}{6} \\ x + \dfrac{9y}{4} = \dfrac{-21}{4} \end{cases}$$

   a. The system is dependent
   b. The system is inconsistent
   c. The system has one unique solution and that solution is
      $(-\dfrac{1}{6}, \dfrac{3}{4})$
   d. The system has one unique solution and that solution is
      $(\dfrac{1}{2}, -5)$
   e. none of these

25. When you solve by the substitution method:

$$y = 5x$$
$$x + y = 12$$

   a. The y-coordinate of the solution is 5
   b. The y-coordinate of the solution is 2
   c. The y-coordinate of the solution is 10
   d. The y-coordinate of the solution is 8
   e. none of these

26. Solve by the substitution method:

$$4x + 5y = 8$$
$$x = 1 - y$$

   a. $(\dfrac{5}{9}, \dfrac{4}{9})$
   b. $(2, 0)$
   c. $(-3, 4)$
   d. $(7, -4)$
   e. none of these

27. Solve by the substitution method:

$$\begin{cases} 5x + 3y = 14 \\ x + 2y = 14 \end{cases}$$

   a. $(1, 3)$
   b. $(-2, 8)$
   c. $(-5, 13)$
   d. $(\dfrac{14}{5}, 0)$
   e. none of these

28. Solve by the <u>substitution method</u>:

$$3x + 5y = 1$$
$$2x + y = -4$$

a. $(2, -1)$
b. $(-8, 5)$
c. $(\frac{1}{3}, \frac{1}{5})$
d. $(-3, 2)$
e. none of these

29. Solve by the <u>substitution method</u>:

$$\begin{cases} \frac{1}{2}x + \frac{3}{4}y = \frac{5}{2} \\ x + 3y = 6 \end{cases}$$

a. $(4, \frac{2}{3})$
b. $(3, 1)$
c. $(15, -3)$
d. $(\frac{1}{2}, -\frac{4}{3})$
e. none of these

30. Solve by the <u>substitution method</u>:

$$\begin{cases} \frac{1}{3}x + \frac{1}{6}y = -\frac{8}{3} \\ x + 5y = 1 \end{cases}$$

a. $(-4, 1)$
b. $(2, -\frac{1}{5})$
c. $(-9, 2)$
d. $(-\frac{17}{2}, 1)$
e. none of these

31. Solve by the <u>substitution method</u>:

$$3x - 2y = 14$$
$$y = \frac{3}{2}x - 7$$

a. The system is dependent
b. The system is inconsistent
c. The system has one unique solution and that solution is
   $(\frac{14}{3}, -7)$
d. The system has one unique solution and that solution is $(0, 7)$
e. none of these

32. Solve by the <u>substitution method</u>:

$$3x + 12y = 5$$
$$4y = 8 - x$$

a. The system has one unique solution and that solution is
   $(\frac{5}{3}, 0)$
b. The system has one unique solution and that solution is (4, 1)
c. The system is dependent
d. The system is inconsistent
e. none of these

33. Solve by the <u>substitution method</u>:

$$5x + 2y = 16$$
$$y = 10 - 2.5x$$

a. The system is dependent
b. The system has one unique solution and that solution is (0, 8)
c. The system is inconsistent
d. The system has one unique solution and that solution is (2, 3)
e. none of these

34. Solve by the <u>substitution method</u>:

$$x + 4y = 16$$
$$y = 4 - 0.25x$$

a. The system is dependent
b. The system has one unique solution and that solution is (16, 4)
c. The system is inconsistent
d. The system has one unique solution and that solution is (0.25, 1)
e. none of these

35. The sum of two numbers is $\frac{3}{5}$. The difference of four times one number and twice the other number is 5. Write a system of equations you could use to find the two numbers.

   a. $xy = \frac{3}{5}$
       $4x + 2y = 5$

   b. $x + y = \frac{3}{5}$
       $4x + 2y = 5$

   c. $x = y + \frac{3}{5}$
       $4x - 2y = 5$

   d. $x + y = \frac{3}{5}$
       $4x - 2y = 5$

   e. none of these

36. The length of a rectangle is 3 cm less than twice its width. The perimeter of the rectangle is 58 cm. Write a system of equations you could use to find the length and width of the rectangle.

   a. $l = 3 - 2w$
      $lw = 58$

   b. $l = 2w - 3$
      $lw = 58$

   c. $l = 3 - 2w$
     $21 + 2w = 58$

   d. $l = 2w - 3$
     $21 + 2w = 58$

   e. none of these

37. The sum of two numbers is 6. The difference of one number and twice the other number is 21. Find the two numbers.

   a. 4 and 3
   b. 8 and -2
   c. 14 and -8
   d. 11 and -5
   e. none of these

208

38. The length of a rectangle is 5 inches more than three times its width. If the perimeter is 74 inches, find the length of the rectangle.

    a. 24 inches
    b. 29 inches
    c. 18 inches
    d. 27 inches
    e. none of these

39. Solution A is 75% salt while solution B is 25% salt. If A and B are to be mixed together to obtain 100 liters of a solution which is 38% salt, how many liters of A are needed?

    a. 21 liters
    b. 26 liters
    c. 32 liters
    d. 34 liters
    e. none of these

40. Ingredient A contains 0.2% hydrocortisone while ingredient B contains 0.6% hydrocortisone. If A and B are to be mixed together to obtain 50 ounces of a mixture that is 0.32% hydrocortisone, how many ounces of ingredient A are needed?

    a. 35 ounces
    b. 38 ounces
    c. 32 ounces
    d. 39 ounces
    e. none of these

41. A boat can travel 36 miles downstream in 4 hours and 25 miles upstream in 5 hours. Find the rate of the boat in still water.

    a. 9 mph
    b. 8 mph
    c. 7 mph
    d. 6 mph
    e. none of these

42. A boat can travel 50 miles upstream in 5 hours and 60 miles downstream in 3 hours. Find the speed of the stream.

    a. 2 mph
    b. 2.5 mph
    c. 3 mph
    d. 3.5 mph
    e. none of these

209

43. A company makes and sells x radios each week with a total weekly cost C, in dollars, given by C = 9x + 3600. The radios are sold for $12 each. Find the break-even level of production.

    a. 400 radios per week
    b. 600 radios per week
    c. 1200 radios per week
    d. 1800 radios per week
    e. none of these

44. A company makes and sells x vases each week with a total weekly cost C, in dollars, given by C = 5x + 840. The vases are sold for $12 each. Find the break-even level of production.

    a. 70 vases per week
    b. 168 vases per week
    c. 90 vases per week
    d. 120 vases per week
    e. none of these

1. ANS:d TYPE:M DIFF:1 SECT:701 OBJ:701 RAND:Y

2. ANS:c TYPE:M DIFF:1 SECT:701 OBJ:701 RAND:Y

3. ANS:c TYPE:M DIFF:1 SECT:701 OBJ:701 RAND:Y

4. ANS:a TYPE:M DIFF:1 SECT:701 OBJ:702 RAND:Y

5. ANS:d TYPE:M DIFF:1 SECT:701 OBJ:703 RAND:Y

6. ANS:c TYPE:M DIFF:2 SECT:701 OBJ:702 RAND:Y

7. ANS:c TYPE:M DIFF:2 SECT:701 OBJ:703 RAND:Y

8. ANS:b TYPE:M DIFF:3 SECT:701 OBJ:704 GRAPH FORMAT:G
   QUESTION GRAPH:1 RAND:Y

9. ANS:c TYPE:M DIFF:3 SECT:701 OBJ:704 GRAPH FORMAT:G
   QUESTION GRAPH:2 RAND:Y

10. ANS:b TYPE:M DIFF:3 SECT:701 OBJ:704 GRAPH FORMAT:G
    QUESTION GRAPH:3 RAND:Y

11. ANS:a TYPE:M DIFF:1 SECT:702 OBJ:705 RAND:Y

12. ANS:c TYPE:M DIFF:1 SECT:702 OBJ:705 RAND:Y

13. ANS:c TYPE:M DIFF:2 SECT:702 OBJ:705 RAND:Y

14. ANS:a TYPE:M DIFF:2 SECT:702 OBJ:705 RAND:Y

15. ANS:b TYPE:M DIFF:3 SECT:702 OBJ:705 RAND:Y

16. ANS:e TYPE:M DIFF:3 SECT:702 OBJ:705 RAND:Y

17. ANS:d TYPE:M DIFF:3 SECT:702 OBJ:705 RAND:Y

```
18. ANS:b   TYPE:M   DIFF:2   SECT:702   OBJ:706   RAND:Y

19. ANS:d   TYPE:M   DIFF:2   SECT:702   OBJ:706   RAND:Y

20. ANS:c   TYPE:M   DIFF:2   SECT:702   OBJ:707   RAND:Y

21. ANS:a   TYPE:M   DIFF:2   SECT:702   OBJ:707   RAND:Y

22. ANS:b   TYPE:M   DIFF:2   SECT:702   OBJ:707   RAND:Y

23. ANS:d   TYPE:M   DIFF:3   SECT:702   OBJ:705   RAND:Y

24. ANS:e   TYPE:M   DIFF:3   SECT:702   OBJ:705   RAND:Y

25. ANS:c   TYPE:M   DIFF:2   SECT:703   OBJ:708   RAND:Y

26. ANS:c   TYPE:M   DIFF:1   SECT:703   OBJ:708   RAND:Y

27. ANS:b   TYPE:M   DIFF:2   SECT:703   OBJ:708   RAND:Y

28. ANS:d   TYPE:M   DIFF:2   SECT:703   OBJ:708   RAND:Y

29. ANS:a   TYPE:M   DIFF:3   SECT:703   OBJ:708   RAND:Y

30. ANS:c   TYPE:M   DIFF:3   SECT:703   OBJ:708   RAND:Y

31. ANS:a   TYPE:M   DIFF:2   SECT:703   OBJ:710   RAND:Y

32. ANS:d   TYPE:M   DIFF:2   SECT:703   OBJ:709   RAND:Y

33. ANS:c   TYPE:M   DIFF:2   SECT:703   OBJ:709   RAND:Y

34. ANS:a   TYPE:M   DIFF:2   SECT:703   OBJ:710   RAND:Y

35. ANS:d   TYPE:M   DIFF:2   SECT:704   OBJ:711   RAND:Y
```

36. ANS:d TYPE:M DIFF:2 SECT:704 OBJ:711 RAND:Y

37. ANS:d TYPE:M DIFF:1 SECT:704 OBJ:712 RAND:Y

38. ANS:b TYPE:M DIFF:2 SECT:704 OBJ:712 RAND:Y

39. ANS:b TYPE:M DIFF:2 SECT:704 OBJ:713 RAND:Y

40. ANS:a TYPE:M DIFF:2 SECT:704 OBJ:713 RAND:Y

41. ANS:c TYPE:M DIFF:2 SECT:704 OBJ:714 RAND:Y

42. ANS:e TYPE:M DIFF:2 SECT:704 OBJ:714 RAND:Y

43. ANS:c TYPE:M DIFF:2 SECT:704 OBJ:715 RAND:Y

44. ANS:d TYPE:M DIFF:2 SECT:704 OBJ:715 RAND:Y

CHAPTER 7C: SYSTEMS OF EQUATIONS

MULTIPLE CHOICE

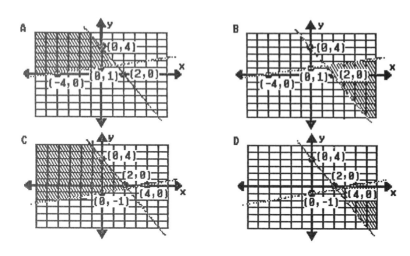

1. Which of the above is a graph of this system of inequalities?

$$2x + y < 4$$
$$x - 4y > 4$$

a. A
b. B
c. C
d. D
e. none of these

216

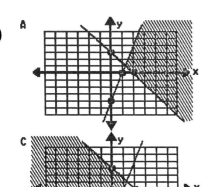

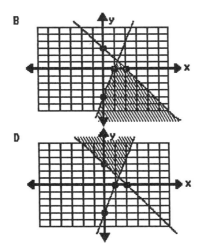

2. Which of the above is a graph of this system of inequalities?

$$3x + 2y \leq 6$$
$$4x - y \leq 4$$

a. A
b. B
c. C
d. D
e. none of these

217

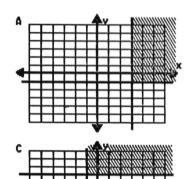
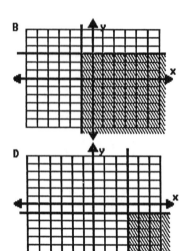

3. Which of the above is a graph of this system of inequalities?

     $x \geq 3$
     $y \leq -1$

a. A
b. B
c. C
d. D
e. none of these

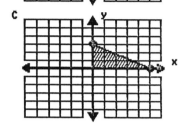

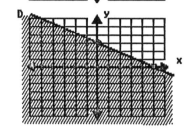

4. Which of the above is a graph of this system of inequalities?

$$3x + 5y \geq 15$$
$$x \geq 0$$
$$y \geq 0$$

a. A
b. B
c. C
d. D
e. none of these

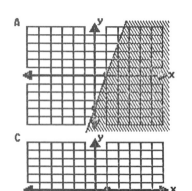

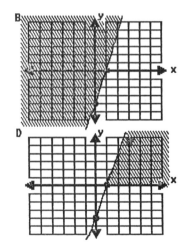

5. Which of the above is a graph of this system?

$$\begin{cases} 4x - y \geq 4 \\ x \geq 0 \\ y \geq 0 \end{cases}$$

a. A
b. B
c. C
d. D
e. none of these

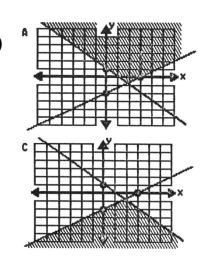
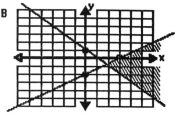
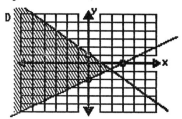

6. Which of the above is a graph of this system?

$$2x - 3y \leq 6$$
$$x + y \geq 1$$

a. A
b. B
c. C
d. D
e. none of these

1. ANS:e TYPE:M DIFF:2 SECT:705 OBJ:716 GRAPH FORMAT:G
   QUESTION GRAPH:1 RAND:Y

2. ANS:c TYPE:M DIFF:2 SECT:705 OBJ:716 GRAPH FORMAT:G
   QUESTION GRAPH:2 RAND:Y

3. ANS:d TYPE:M DIFF:1 SECT:705 OBJ:716 GRAPH FORMAT:G
   QUESTION GRAPH:3 RAND:Y

4. ANS:b TYPE:M DIFF:2 SECT:705 OBJ:716 GRAPH FORMAT:G
   QUESTION GRAPH:4 RAND:Y

5. ANS:d TYPE:M DIFF:2 SECT:705 OBJ:716 GRAPH FORMAT:G
   QUESTION GRAPH:5 RAND:Y

6. ANS:a TYPE:M DIFF:2 SECT:705 OBJ:716 GRAPH FORMAT:G
   QUESTION GRAPH:6 RAND:Y

CHAPTER 8: ROOTS AND RADICALS

SHORT ANSWER

1. Find the two square roots of 81.

2. Evaluate $-\sqrt{\dfrac{9}{25}}$

3. Evaluate $\sqrt{64}$

4. Evaluate $\sqrt[4]{16}$

5. Evaluate $\sqrt[4]{-16}$

6. Simplify (assume that all variables are positive):

$$\sqrt{25a^4 b^2}$$

7. Simplify (assume that all variables are positive):

$$\sqrt[3]{8x^6 y^9 z^3}$$

8. **Simplify** (assume that all variables are positive):

$$\sqrt[4]{s^8 y^{16}}$$

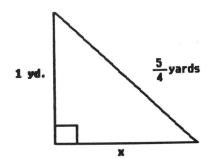

9. **Solve for x:**

10. The formula for the period T of a pendulum when the length l is measured in meters is given by

$$T = 2\pi \sqrt{\dfrac{1}{9.8}} \quad \text{seconds}$$

Find the period of a pendulum 0.2 meters in length (exact answer).

11. Simplify: $\sqrt{75}$

12. Simplify: $\sqrt[4]{48}$

13. Simplify (assume all variables are positive):

$$\sqrt{8x^3 y}$$

14. Simplify (assume all variables are positive):

$$\sqrt{12st^5}$$

15. Simplify (assume all variables are positive):

$$\sqrt[4]{w^6 z^9}$$

16. Simplify $\sqrt{\dfrac{6}{49}}$

17. Simplify (assume all variables are positive):

$$\sqrt[3]{\dfrac{x^2}{8y^6}}$$

18. Simplify $\sqrt{6}\ \sqrt{15}$

19. Simplify (assume all variables are positive):
$$\sqrt{2x}\ \sqrt{10xy}$$

20. Rationalize the denominator (assume all variables are positive):

$$\dfrac{5}{\sqrt{6}}$$

21. Rationalize the denominator (assume all variables are positive):

$$\dfrac{w}{\sqrt{2t}}$$

22. Rationalize the denominator (assume all variables are positive):

$$\dfrac{4}{\sqrt[3]{s}}$$

23. Simplify (assume all variables are positive):

$$\sqrt{\dfrac{3x}{5y}}$$

24. Simplify (assume all variables are positive):

$$\sqrt{\frac{12x^2}{y}}$$

25. Simplify: $5\sqrt{w} + 3\sqrt{w}$

26. Simplify: $\sqrt{27} - \sqrt{50} + \sqrt{300}$

27. Simplify: $5\sqrt{6} + \sqrt{18} - 4\sqrt{24}$

28. Simplify: $3\sqrt{z^5} + 2\sqrt{z^6} + z\sqrt{z^3}$

29. Combine as a single fraction & simplify:

$$\frac{\sqrt{75}}{2} - \frac{\sqrt{12}}{5}$$

30. Combine as a single fraction & simplify:

$$\frac{5}{\sqrt{3}} - 1$$

31. Multiply and simplify: $\sqrt{3}(\sqrt{5} + \sqrt{10})$

32. Multiply and simplify: $(\sqrt{6} - \sqrt{7})\sqrt{14}$

33. Multiply and simplify (assume that the variables represent positive real numbers):

$$\sqrt{2x}(\sqrt{6x} - \sqrt{22})$$

34. Multiply and simplify (assume that the variables represent positive real numbers):

$$(\sqrt{x} + 5)(\sqrt{x} - 3)$$

35. Rationalize the denominator and simplify:

$$\frac{3}{\sqrt{5} - 4}$$

36. Rationalize the denominator and simplify (assume that all variables are positive):

$$\frac{3y}{\sqrt{y} + 2}$$

226

37. Rationalize the denominator and simplify:

$$\frac{5\sqrt{2} + 2}{\sqrt{2} + 6}$$

38. Rationalize the denominator and simplify:

$$\frac{7\sqrt{5} + 3}{3 - \sqrt{5}}$$

39. Solve: $\sqrt{t + 5} = 3$

40. Solve: $\sqrt{w + 12} = w + 6$

41. Solve: $\sqrt{2x - 1} + 2 = x$

42. Solve: $\sqrt{3y - 5} = y - 3$

43. Evaluate: $64^{\frac{2}{3}}$

44. Evaluate: $16^{-\frac{1}{2}} - 8^{-\frac{2}{3}}$

45. Use the properties of exponents to simplify (write the answer using only positive exponents):

$$5^{\frac{2}{5}} \cdot 5^{\frac{1}{2}}$$

46. Use the properties of exponents to simplify (write the answer using only positive exponents):

$$\frac{x^{\frac{3}{4}}}{x^{\frac{1}{8}}}$$

47. Replace all radicals with rational exponents and simplify (answer in exponential form):

$$\frac{\sqrt[3]{b^2}}{\sqrt{b}}$$

48. Write as an imaginary number: $\sqrt{-25}$

227

49. Perform the indicated operation and answer in the form a + bi:

$$(5 + 2i)^2$$

50. Perform the indicated operation and answer in the form a + bi:

$$(2 + 9i)^2$$

MULTIPLE CHOICE

51. Find the two square roots of 16

a. 16 and 1
b. -16 and -1
c. 4 and -4
d. 8 and -8
e. none of these

52. Evaluate: $-\sqrt{\dfrac{16}{81}}$

a. $-\dfrac{4}{9}$
b. $\dfrac{4}{9}$
c. no real number answer
d. $-\dfrac{8}{81}$
e. none of these

53. Evaluate: $\sqrt{49}$

a. 7 and -7
b. 7 only
c. -7 only
d. no real number answer
e. none of these

54. Evaluate $\sqrt[3]{64}$

a. 8
b. 16
c. 4
d. 2
e. none of these

228

55. Evaluate $\sqrt[4]{-1}$

   a. -1
   b. 1
   c. $-\frac{1}{4}$
   d. no real number answer
   e. none of these

56. Simplify (assume all variables represent positive real numbers):

   $$\sqrt{9x^6 y^4}$$

   a. $3x^2 y$
   b. $3x^3 y^2$
   c. $3x^6 y^4$
   d. $3x^4 y^2$
   e. none of these

57. Simplify (assume all variables represent positive real numbers):

   $$\sqrt[3]{27x^6 w^3}$$

   a. $3x^3 w \sqrt[3]{w}$
   b. $3x^3 w$
   c. $3x^3 w^2$
   d. $3x^2 w \sqrt[3]{w}$
   e. none of these

58. Simplify (assume that all variables represent positive real numbers):

   $$\sqrt[5]{y^{15} m^{10}}$$

   a. $y^{10} m^5$
   b. $y^7 m^5 \sqrt[5]{y}$
   c. $y^3 m^5$
   d. $y^3 m^2$
   e. none of these

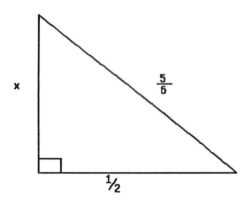

59. In the above diagram, solve for x.

   a. $\frac{1}{3}$

   b. $\frac{17}{18}$

   c. $\frac{2}{3}$

   d. $\frac{5}{8}$

   e. none of these

60. The formula for the period T of a pendulum when the length l is measured in meters is given by:

$$T = 2\pi\sqrt{\frac{l}{9.8}} \quad \text{seconds}$$

Find the period of a pendulum 0.098 meters in length.

   a. 2π seconds
   b. 20π seconds
   c. $(0.2)\pi$ seconds
   d. 200π seconds
   e. none of these

61. Simplify: $\sqrt{48}$

   a. $4\sqrt{3}$

   b. $3\sqrt{2}$

   c. $16\sqrt{3}$

   d. $2\sqrt{12}$

   e. none of these

62. Simplify: $\sqrt[3]{40}$

    a. $2\sqrt[3]{10}$
    b. $2\sqrt{10}$
    c. $2\sqrt[3]{5}$
    d. $2\sqrt{5}$
    e. none of these

63. Simplify (assume all variables are positive):

$$\sqrt{50w^5 y^3}$$

    a. $5\sqrt{2w^5 y^3}$
    b. $2wy\sqrt{5wy}$
    c. $5w^4 y\sqrt{2wy}$
    d. $5w^3 y\sqrt{2wy}$
    e. none of these

64. Simplify (assume all variables are positive):

$$\sqrt{18wt^3}$$

    a. $3\sqrt{2wt^3}$
    b. $3t\sqrt{2w}$
    c. $3t^2\sqrt{2w}$
    d. $3t\sqrt{2wt}$
    e. none of these

65. Simplify (assume all variables are positive):
$$\sqrt[5]{x^7 l^{11}}$$

    a. $x^3 l^5 \sqrt[5]{xl}$
    b. $xl^2 \sqrt[5]{x^2 l}$
    c. $x^2 l^6 \sqrt[5]{xl}$
    d. $x^2 l^2 \sqrt[5]{xl^3}$
    e. none of these

66. Simplify $\sqrt{\dfrac{10}{81}}$

   a. $\dfrac{5}{9}$

   b. $\dfrac{\sqrt{10}}{81}$

   c. $\dfrac{10}{9}$

   d. $\dfrac{\sqrt{10}}{9}$

   e. None of these

67. Simplify (assume all variables are positive):

   $$\sqrt[4]{\dfrac{x^3}{16w^8}}$$

   a. $\dfrac{x\sqrt[4]{x}}{4w^4}$

   b. $\dfrac{\sqrt[4]{x^3}}{4w^2}$

   c. $\dfrac{\sqrt[4]{x^3}}{2w^4}$

   d. $\dfrac{\sqrt[4]{x^3}}{2w^2}$

   e. none of these

68. Simplify: $\sqrt{10}\ \sqrt{15}$

   a. $\sqrt{150}$

   b. 5

   c. $5\sqrt{6}$

   d. $5\sqrt{30}$

   e. none of these

69. Simplify (assume all variables are positive):

   $$\sqrt{3t}\ \sqrt{15tm}$$

   a. $t\sqrt{45m}$

   b. $45t^2\sqrt{m}$

   c. $5t\sqrt{3m}$

   d. $3t\sqrt{5m}$

   e. none of these

70. Rationalize the denominator: $\dfrac{11}{\sqrt{10}}$

    a. 11

    b. $\dfrac{11}{100}$

    c. $\dfrac{11\sqrt{10}}{10}$

    d. $\dfrac{11\sqrt{10}}{100}$

    e. None of these

71. Rationalize the denominator (assume all variables are positive):

$$\frac{x}{\sqrt{3m}}$$

    a. $\dfrac{x\sqrt{3m}}{3m}$

    b. $\dfrac{x\sqrt{3m}}{9m^2}$

    c. $\dfrac{x^2}{3m}$

    d. $3xm$

    e. none of these

72. Rationalize the denominator (assume all variables are positive):

$$\frac{10}{\sqrt[3]{t}}$$

    a. $\dfrac{1000}{t}$

    b. $\dfrac{10\,\sqrt[3]{t}}{t}$

    c. $\dfrac{10\,\sqrt[3]{t}}{t^2}$

    d. $\dfrac{10\,\sqrt[3]{t^2}}{t}$

    e. none of these

73. Simplify (assume all variables are positive):

$$\sqrt{\frac{5w}{6t}}$$

a. $\dfrac{\sqrt{5w}}{6t}$

b. $\dfrac{\sqrt{30wt}}{6t}$

c. $\dfrac{\sqrt{30wt}}{36t^2}$

d. $\dfrac{25w^2}{36t^2}$

e. none of these

74. Simplify (assume all variables are positive)

$$\sqrt{\frac{18m^2}{1}}$$

a. $\dfrac{3m\sqrt{2}}{1}$

b. $3m1\sqrt{2}$

c. $\dfrac{3m\sqrt{21}}{1^2}$

d. $\dfrac{3m^2(\sqrt{21})}{1}$

e. none of these

75. Simplify: $2\sqrt{c} + 3\sqrt{c}$

a. $5c$

b. $6c$

c. $5\sqrt{2c}$

d. $10\sqrt{c}$

e. none of these

76. Simplify: $\sqrt{20} - \sqrt{18} + \sqrt{45}$

    a. $2\sqrt{3}$

    b. $\sqrt{47}$

    c. $5\sqrt{5} - 3\sqrt{2}$

    d. $2\sqrt{2} + 5\sqrt{3}$

    e. none of these

77. Simplify: $4\sqrt{8} + 2\sqrt{12} - \sqrt{200}$

    a. $4\sqrt{3} - 2\sqrt{2}$

    b. $12\sqrt{5} - 10\sqrt{2}$

    c. -12

    d. $-4\sqrt{2} + 5\sqrt{3}$

    e. none of these

78. Simplify: $5\sqrt{x^6} + 2\sqrt{x^3} + 5x\sqrt{x}$

    a. $(5x + 7)\sqrt{x^{10}}$

    b. $7x\sqrt{x} + 5x^3$

    c. $(7x^4 + 5x)\sqrt{x}$

    d. $5x^4 + 7x\sqrt{2x}$

    e. none of these

79. Combine as a single fraction and simplify:

$$\frac{\sqrt{50}}{3} + \frac{\sqrt{8}}{5}$$

    a. $\dfrac{7\sqrt{2}}{15}$

    b. $\dfrac{\sqrt{58}}{15}$

    c. $\dfrac{31\sqrt{2}}{15}$

    d. $\dfrac{8\sqrt{58}}{15}$

    e. none of these

80. Combine as a single fraction & simplify: $\dfrac{3}{\sqrt{11}} - 2$

    a. $\dfrac{3-2\sqrt{11}}{11}$

    b. $\dfrac{3\sqrt{11} - 22}{11}$

    c. $\dfrac{-19}{11}$

    d. $\dfrac{-13}{11}$

    e. none of these

81. Multiply and simplify: $\sqrt{2}\,(\sqrt{3} + \sqrt{15})$

    a. $\sqrt{6} + \sqrt{30}$
    b. 6
    c. $\sqrt{6} + \sqrt{15}$
    d. $2\sqrt{5}$
    e. none of these

82. Multiply and simplify: $(\sqrt{15} - \sqrt{7})\,\sqrt{21}$

    a. $2\sqrt{42}$
    b. $3\sqrt{35} - 7\sqrt{3}$
    c. $\sqrt{315} - \sqrt{147}$
    d. $3\sqrt{7} - 7\sqrt{3}$
    e. none of these

83. Multiply and simplify (assume that the variables represent positive real numbers):

    $\sqrt{5x}\,(\sqrt{10x} - \sqrt{55})$

    a. $5\sqrt{2x} - 5\sqrt{11x}$
    b. $5x\sqrt{2} - \sqrt{55}$
    c. $5x\sqrt{2} - 5\sqrt{11x}$
    d. $5\sqrt{2x} - \sqrt{55}$
    e. none of these

84. Multiply and simplify (assume that the variables represent positive real numbers):

$$(\sqrt{w} + 8)(\sqrt{w} - 9)$$

a. $w - 72$
b. $w - \sqrt{2w} - 72$
c. $w^2 - \sqrt{2w} - 72$
d. $w - \sqrt{w} - 72$
e. none of these

85. Rationalize the denominator and simplify:

$$\frac{5}{\sqrt{3} - 8}$$

a. $\dfrac{-5(\sqrt{3} + 8)}{61}$

b. $\dfrac{-\sqrt{3} - 8}{11}$

c. $\dfrac{5(\sqrt{3} - 8)}{67}$

d. $\dfrac{5(\sqrt{3} + 8)}{73}$

e. none of these

86. Rationalize the denominator and simplify (assume that all variables are positive):

$$\frac{5t}{\sqrt{t} + 3}$$

a. $\dfrac{5t \sqrt{t}}{t + 3}$

b. $\dfrac{5t (\sqrt{t} + 3)}{t + 9}$

c. $\dfrac{5t (\sqrt{t} - 3)}{t - 9}$

d. $\dfrac{5t (\sqrt{t} - 3)}{t - 3}$

e. none of these

237

87. Rationalize the denominator and simplify:

$$\frac{3\sqrt{5} + 1}{\sqrt{5} + 3}$$

a. 1
b. $12 + 2\sqrt{5}$
c. $-3 - 8\sqrt{5}$
d. $2\sqrt{5} + 3$
e. none of these

88. Rationalize the denominator and simplify:

$$\frac{5\sqrt{11} + 3}{5 - \sqrt{11}}$$

a. $2\sqrt{11} + 5$
b. $2\sqrt{11}$
c. $\frac{14\sqrt{11} + 35}{18}$
d. $\frac{-14\sqrt{11}}{3}$
e. none of these

89. Solve: $\sqrt{y - 8} = 2$

a. 10 only
b. 12 only
c. 14 only
d. 16 only
e. none of these

90. Solve: $\sqrt{x + 9} = x + 3$

a. 0 only
b. $\{0, +5\}$
c. $\{0, -5\}$
d. $\{0, 1\}$
e. none of these

238

91. Solve $\sqrt{3x - 1} + 2 = 3x - 1$

    a. no solution
    b. $\frac{5}{3}$ only
    c. $\frac{2}{3}$ only
    d. $\{\frac{5}{3}, \frac{2}{3}\}$
    e. none of these

92. Solve: $\sqrt{2y + 1} = y - 7$

    a. all of the solutions are between 8 and 30
    b. all of the solutions are between -4 and 16
    c. all of the solutions are between 20 and 50
    d. all of the solutions are between -10 and 10
    e. none of these

93. Evaluate: $16^{\frac{3}{4}}$

    a. 12
    b. 8
    c. 6
    d. 2
    e. none of these

94. Evaluate: $4^{-\frac{1}{2}} - 64^{-\frac{1}{3}}$

    a. 2
    b. -6
    c. $\frac{1}{4}$
    d. $\frac{1}{2}$
    e. none of these

95. Use the properties of exponents to simplify (write the answer using only positive exponents):

    $$6^{\frac{1}{4}} \cdot 6^{\frac{2}{3}}$$

    a. $6^{\frac{1}{6}}$
    b. $36^{\frac{1}{6}}$
    c. $6^{\frac{11}{12}}$
    d. $36^{\frac{11}{12}}$
    e. none of these

239

96. Use the properties of exponents to simplify (write the answer using only positive exponents):

$$\frac{y^{\frac{5}{6}}}{y^{\frac{1}{3}}}$$

   a. $y^{\frac{5}{2}}$

   b. $y^{\frac{1}{2}}$

   c. $y^{\frac{7}{6}}$

   d. $y^{\frac{5}{18}}$
   e. none of these

97. Replace all radicals with rational exponents and simplify (answer in exponential form):

$$\frac{\sqrt[4]{x^3}}{\sqrt[3]{x}}$$

   a. $x^{\frac{5}{12}}$

   b. $x^{\frac{1}{4}}$

   c. $x^{\frac{4}{7}}$

   d. $x^{\frac{1}{2}}$
   e. none of these

98. Write as an imaginary number: $\sqrt{-4}$

   a. 4i
   b. -4i
   c. 2i
   d. -2i
   e. none of these

99. Perform the indicated operation and answer in the form
a + bi: $(3 + 5i)^2$

   a. 34 + 30i
   b. -16 + oi
   c. 9 + 55i
   d. 9 + 25i
   e. none of these

100. Perform the indicated operation and answer in the form
a + bi: $(5 + 6i)^2$

   a. 25 + 96i
   b. 25 + 36i
   c. 61 + 60i
   d. -11 + 60i
   e. none of these

1. ANS:9 and -9   TYPE:S   DIFF:1   SECT:801   OBJ:801   RAND:Y

2. TYPE:S   DIFF:2   SECT:801   OBJ:802   RAND:Y

ANSWER:
$-\frac{3}{5}$

3. ANS:8   TYPE:S   DIFF:2   SECT:801   OBJ:802   RAND:Y

4. ANS:2   TYPE:S   DIFF:2   SECT:801   OBJ:803   RAND:Y

5. TYPE:S   DIFF:3   SECT:801   OBJ:803   RAND:Y

ANSWER:
   not a real number

6. TYPE:S   DIFF:2   SECT:801   OBJ:804   RAND:Y

ANSWER:
   $5a^2 b$

7. TYPE:S   DIFF:2   SECT:801   OBJ:804   RAND:Y

ANSWER:
   $2x^2 y^3 z$

8. TYPE:S   DIFF:2   SECT:801   OBJ:804   RAND:Y

ANSWER:
   $s^2 y^4$

9. TYPE:S   DIFF:3   SECT:801   OBJ:805   GRAPH FORMAT:G
   QUESTION GRAPH:1   RAND:Y

ANSWER:
   $\frac{3}{4}$ yards

10. TYPE:S   DIFF:3   SECT:801   OBJ:805   RAND:Y

ANSWER:
   $\frac{2\pi}{7}$ seconds

242

11. TYPE:S DIFF:1 SECT:802 OBJ:806 RAND:Y

ANSWER:
$$5\sqrt{3}$$

12. TYPE:S DIFF:2 SECT:802 OBJ:806 RAND:Y

ANSWER:
$$2\sqrt[4]{3}$$

13. TYPE:S DIFF:2 SECT:802 OBJ:806 RAND:Y

ANSWER:
$$2x\sqrt{2xy}$$

14. TYPE:S DIFF:2 SECT:802 OBJ:806 RAND:Y

ANSWER:
$$2t^2\sqrt{3st}$$

15. TYPE:S DIFF:2 SECT:802 OBJ:806 RAND:Y

ANSWER:
$$wz^2\sqrt[4]{w^2\,z}$$

16. TYPE:S DIFF:1 SECT:802 OBJ:807 RAND:Y

ANSWER:
$$\frac{\sqrt{6}}{7}$$

17. TYPE:S DIFF:3 SECT:802 OBJ:807 RAND:Y

ANSWER:
$$\frac{\sqrt[3]{x^2}}{2y^2}$$

18. TYPE:S DIFF:1 SECT:802 OBJ:808 RAND:Y

ANSWER:
$$3\sqrt{10}$$

19. TYPE:S DIFF:2 SECT:802 OBJ:808 RAND:Y

ANSWER:

$$2x\sqrt{5y}$$

20. TYPE:S DIFF:2 SECT:802 OBJ:809 RAND:Y

ANSWER:

$$\frac{5\sqrt{6}}{6}$$

21. TYPE:S DIFF:2 SECT:802 OBJ:809 RAND:Y

ANSWER:

$$\frac{w\sqrt{2t}}{2t}$$

22. TYPE:S DIFF:3 SECT:802 OBJ:809 RAND:Y

ANSWER:

$$\frac{4\sqrt[3]{s^2}}{s}$$

23. TYPE:S DIFF:2 SECT:802 OBJ:810 RAND:Y

ANSWER:

$$\frac{\sqrt{15xy}}{5y}$$

24. TYPE:S DIFF:3 SECT:802 OBJ:810 RAND:Y

ANSWER:

$$\frac{2x\sqrt{3y}}{y}$$

25. TYPE:S DIFF:1 SECT:803 OBJ:811 RAND:Y

ANSWER:

$$8\sqrt{w}$$

26. TYPE:S DIFF:2 SECT:803 OBJ:811 RAND:Y

ANSWER:

$13\sqrt{3} - 5\sqrt{2}$

27. TYPE:S DIFF:2 SECT:803 OBJ:811 RAND:Y

ANSWER:

$3\sqrt{2} - 3\sqrt{6}$

28. TYPE:S DIFF:3 SECT:803 OBJ:811 RAND:Y

ANSWER:

$4z^2 (\sqrt{z}) + 2z^3$

29. TYPE:S DIFF:2 SECT:803 OBJ:812 RAND:Y

ANSWER:

$\dfrac{21\sqrt{3}}{10}$

30. TYPE:S DIFF:2 SECT:803 OBJ:812 RAND:Y

ANSWER:

$\dfrac{5\sqrt{3} - 3}{3}$

31. TYPE:S DIFF:1 SECT:804 OBJ:813 RAND:Y

ANSWER:

$\sqrt{15} + \sqrt{30}$

32. TYPE:S DIFF:2 SECT:804 OBJ:813 RAND:Y

ANSWER:

$2\sqrt{21} - 7\sqrt{2}$

33. TYPE:S DIFF:2 SECT:804 OBJ:813 RAND:Y

ANSWER:

$2x\sqrt{3} - 2\sqrt{11x}$

245

34. TYPE:S DIFF:2 SECT:804 OBJ:813 RAND:Y

ANSWER:

$x + 2\sqrt{x} - 15$

35. TYPE:S DIFF:2 SECT:804 OBJ:814 RAND:Y

ANSWER:

$$\frac{-3(\sqrt{5} + 4)}{11}$$

36. TYPE:S DIFF:2 SECT:804 OBJ:814 RAND:Y

ANSWER:

$$\frac{3y\ (\sqrt{y} - 2)}{y - 4}$$

37. TYPE:S DIFF:3 SECT:804 OBJ:814 RAND:Y

ANSWER:

$$\frac{1 + 14\sqrt{2}}{17}$$

38. TYPE:S DIFF:3 SECT:804 OBJ:814 RAND:Y

ANSWER:

$11 + 6\sqrt{5}$

39. ANS:4 TYPE:S DIFF:1 SECT:805 OBJ:815 RAND:Y

40. ANS:-3 TYPE:S DIFF:2 SECT:805 OBJ:815 RAND:Y

41. ANS:5 TYPE:S DIFF:3 SECT:805 OBJ:815 RAND:Y

42. ANS:7 TYPE:S DIFF:2 SECT:805 OBJ:815 RAND:Y

43. ANS:16 TYPE:S DIFF:2 SECT:806 OBJ:816 RAND:Y

44. TYPE:S DIFF:3 SECT:806 OBJ:816 RAND:Y

45. TYPE:S DIFF:2 SECT:806 OBJ:817 RAND:Y

ANSWER:
$$5^{\frac{9}{10}}$$

46. TYPE:S DIFF:2 SECT:806 OBJ:817 RAND:Y

ANSWER:
$$x^{\frac{5}{8}}$$

47. TYPE:S DIFF:3 SECT:806 OBJ:817 RAND:Y

ANSWER:
$$b^{\frac{1}{6}}$$

48. ANS:5i TYPE:S DIFF:1 SECT:807 OBJ:818 RAND:Y

49. ANS:21 + 20i TYPE:S DIFF:2 SECT:807 OBJ:819 RAND:Y

50. ANS:-77 + 36i TYPE:S DIFF:2 SECT:807 OBJ:819 RAND:Y

51. ANS:c TYPE:M DIFF:1 SECT:801 OBJ:801 RAND:Y

52. ANS:a TYPE:M DIFF:2 SECT:801 OBJ:802 RAND:Y

53. ANS:b TYPE:M DIFF:2 SECT:801 OBJ:802 RAND:Y

54. ANS:c TYPE:M DIFF:2 SECT:801 OBJ:803 RAND:Y

55. ANS:d TYPE:M DIFF:3 SECT:801 OBJ:803 RAND:Y

56. ANS:b TYPE:M DIFF:2 SECT:801 OBJ:804 RAND:Y

57. ANS:e TYPE:M DIFF:2 SECT:801 OBJ:804 RAND:Y

58. ANS:d TYPE:M DIFF:2 SECT:801 OBJ:804 RAND:Y

59. ANS:c TYPE:M DIFF:3 SECT:801 OBJ:805 GRAPH FORMAT:G
    QUESTION GRAPH:2 RAND:Y

60. ANS:c TYPE:M DIFF:3 SECT:801 OBJ:805 RAND:Y

61. ANS:a TYPE:M DIFF:1 SECT:802 OBJ:806 RAND:Y

62. ANS:c TYPE:M DIFF:2 SECT:802 OBJ:806 RAND:Y

63. ANS:e TYPE:M DIFF:2 SECT:802 OBJ:806 RAND:Y

64. ANS:d TYPE:M DIFF:2 SECT:802 OBJ:806 RAND:Y

65. ANS:b TYPE:M DIFF:2 SECT:802 OBJ:806 RAND:Y

66. ANS:d TYPE:M DIFF:1 SECT:802 OBJ:807 RAND:Y

67. ANS:d TYPE:M DIFF:3 SECT:802 OBJ:807 RAND:Y

68. ANS:c TYPE:M DIFF:1 SECT:802 OBJ:808 RAND:Y

69. ANS:d TYPE:M DIFF:2 SECT:802 OBJ:808 RAND:Y

70. ANS:c TYPE:M DIFF:2 SECT:802 OBJ:809 RAND:Y

71. ANS:a TYPE:M DIFF:2 SECT:802 OBJ:809 RAND:Y

72. ANS:d TYPE:M DIFF:3 SECT:802 OBJ:809 RAND:Y

73. ANS:b TYPE:M DIFF:2 SECT:802 OBJ:810 RAND:Y

74. ANS:e TYPE:M DIFF:3 SECT:802 OBJ:810 RAND:Y

75. ANS:e TYPE:M DIFF:1 SECT:803 OBJ:811 RAND:Y

76. ANS:c TYPE:M DIFF:2 SECT:803 OBJ:811 RAND:Y

CHAPTER 9:   QUADRATIC EQUATIONS

SHORT ANSWER

1. Solve by the square root method (simplify your answer):

$$w^2 = \frac{9}{16}$$

2. Solve by the square root method (simplify your answer):

$$y^2 = 35$$

3. Solve by the square root method (simplify your answer):

$$t^2 = 24$$

4. Solve by the square root method (simplify your answer):

$$(y + 4)^2 = 25$$

5. Solve by the square root method (simplify your answer):

$$(m - 3)^2 = 48$$

6. Solve by the square root method (simplify your answer):

$$(q + 9)^2 = 48$$

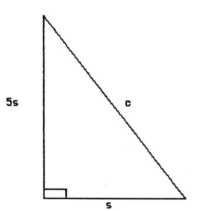

7. From the above right triangle, express s in terms of c (simplify your answer)

8. Solve for y: $M = \pi y^2 t$

9. What constant must be added to $x^2 - 12x$ to make a perfect square trinomial?

10. What constant must be added to $y^2 + \frac{3}{5} y$ to make a perfect square trinomial?

250

11. Solve <u>by completing the square</u>: $x^2 + 2x = 15$

12. Solve <u>by completing the square</u>: $y^2 - 6y = 16$

13. Solve <u>by completing the square</u>: $m^2 - 5m = -3$

14. Solve <u>by completing the square</u>: $r^2 - 9r = 2$

15. Solve <u>by completing the square</u>: $2x^2 + 5x - 5 = 0$

16. Solve <u>by completing the square</u> (simplify your answer):

   $3n^2 - 4n - 2 = 0$

17. Write the following quadratic equation in standard form
   $ax^2 + bx + c = 0$ with $a > 0$, and identify a, b, and c:

   $5x^2 = 3x - 4$

18. Write the following quadratic equation in standard form
   $ax^2 + bx + c = 0$ with $a > 0$, and identify a, b, and c:

   $4 = x(3 - 2x)$

19. Use the <u>quadratic formula</u> to solve: $x^2 - 3x - 7 = 0$

20. Use the <u>quadratic formula</u> to solve:

   $y^2 - 7y - 2 = 0$

21. Use the <u>quadratic formula</u> to solve (simplify your answer):

   $m^2 - 3m = 9$

22. Use the <u>quadratic formula</u> to solve (simplify your answer):

   $x^2 + 7x = -1$

23. Use the <u>quadratic formula</u> to solve (simplify your answer):

   $2x^2 = 3 - 6x$

24. Use the <u>quadratic formula</u> to solve (simplify your answer):

   $3x^2 = 6x - 2$

25. Use any appropriate algebraic method to solve:

   $x(x - 1) = 20$

26. Use any appropriate algebraic method to solve:

   $x(x - 9) = 4$

27. Find all solutions, both real and complex, to:

$$y^2 + 3y + 15 = 0$$

(write all complex number solutions in standard form a $\pm$ bi)

28. Find all solutions, both real and complex, to:

$$m^2 + 5m + 12 = 0$$

(write all complex number solutions in standard form a $\pm$ bi)

29. Find all solutions, both real and complex, to:

$$x(x - 2) = -6$$

(simplify all answers and **write complex number solutions in the form a $\pm$ bi**)

30. Use the discriminant to determine if the roots are real or complex. Also determine the number of roots. Do <u>not</u> solve the equation.

$$5m^2 - 3m + 8 = 0$$

31. Use the discriminant to determine if the roots are real or complex. Also determine the number of roots. Do <u>not</u> solve the equation.

$$3q^2 - 5q - 15 = 0$$

32. The difference of a number and its reciprocal is $\frac{8}{3}$. Find all possible values for the number and write the reciprocal next to the number in your answer.

33. The difference of a number and its reciprocal is $\frac{7}{12}$. Find all possible values for the number and write the reciprocal next to the number in your answer.

34. Potter's Barn makes and sells x bowls each day. **The daily cost** C is given by $C = \frac{1}{10} x^2 + 350$ and the daily **revenue R is given by** R = 12x. The company cannot make more than 65 **bowls each day.** Find the break-even point for the company.

35. One number is three times another number and **their product is 36.** Find the two numbers (there are two answers). Simplify your answers.

36. A car that was involved in an accident left skid **marks measuring** 200 feet. The braking distance d for this particular **make of car** can be approximated by $d = \frac{1}{10} v^2 + 5$, where v is the speed of the car. What was the speed of the car at the time of the accident?

37. If an object is dropped, the distance d dropped in terms of the speed v is d = $\frac{v^2}{64}$, where d is in feet and v is in feet per second. An object is dropped from an airplane flying at 2000 feet. What is the speed of the object when it hits the ground?

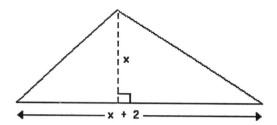

38. The base of a triangle is 2 inches more than its height (refer to the above diagram). If the area is $4\frac{1}{2}$ square inches, find the length of the base and the height.

39. An open box is to be made from a square sheet of cardboard by cutting squares measuring 4 inches on a side from each corner and folding up the sides. If the required volume is 120 cubic inches, what size piece of cardboard is needed to make the box?

40. Find the coordinates of the vertex for y = (x - 5)²

41. Find the coordinates of the vertex for y = 3(x + 2)² - 5

42. Find the coordinates of the vertex for y = 5(x - 3)² + 4

43. Complete the square to put the following equation in the form

    y = a(x - h)² + k:

    y = x² + 18x + 78

44. Complete the square to put the following equation in the form
    y = a(x - h)² + k:

    y = 3x² + 24x + 40

45. Find the vertex for y = x² + 6x + 7

46. Find the vertex for y = -x² + 8x - 11

47. Find the vertex for y = x² + 10x + 33

48. Find the vertex for y = -3x² + 12x - 8

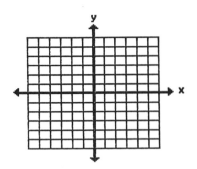

49. On the above coordinate plane, graph $y = -(x + 2)^2 + 3$ (label the vertex).

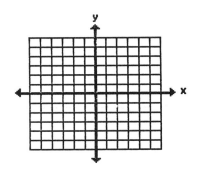

50. On the above coordinate plane, graph $y = 2x^2 - 4x - 2$ (label the vertex).

MULTIPLE CHOICE

51. Solve by the square root method (simplify your answer):

$$y^2 = \frac{25}{49}$$

a. $y = \frac{5}{7}$ only

b. $y = \frac{25}{49}$ only

c. $y = \pm\frac{5}{7}$

d. $y = \pm\frac{25}{49}$

e. none of these

52. Solve by the square root method (simplify your answer):

$m^2 = 43$

a. $m = \pm 43$
b. $m = \pm\sqrt{43}$
c. $m = \sqrt{43}$
d. $m = 43$
e. none of these

53. Solve by the square root method (simplify your answer):

$w^2 = 54$

a. $w = \pm 54$
b. $w = \pm\sqrt{54}$
c. $w = \pm 3\sqrt{6}$
d. $w = 3\pm\sqrt{6}$
e. none of these

54. Solve by the square root method (simplify your answer):

$x^2 = 60$

a. $x = \sqrt{60}$
b. $x = \pm\sqrt{60}$
c. $x = 2\pm\sqrt{15}$
d. $x = \pm 2\sqrt{15}$
e. none of these

55. Solve by the square root method (simplify your answer):

$(t + 8)^2 = 49$

a. $t = \pm 7$
b. $t = 15$ or $t = 1$
c. $t = 41$ or $t = 57$
d. $t = -8 \pm(49)^2$
e. none of these

56. Solve by the square root method (simplify your answer):

$$(x - 5)^2 = 19$$

a. $x = -14$ or $x = 24$
b. $x = \pm\sqrt{19}$
c. $x = \pm 5\sqrt{19}$
d. $x = 5 \pm \sqrt{19}$
e. none of these

57. Solve by the square root method (simplify your answer):

$$(m + 6)^2 = 32$$

a. $m = \pm\sqrt{32}$
b. $m = \pm 4\sqrt{2}$
c. $m = -6 \pm 4\sqrt{2}$
d. $m = -10\sqrt{2}$ or $m = -2\sqrt{2}$
e. none of these

58. Solve by the square root method (simplify your answer):

$$(q + 12)^2 = 24$$

a. $q = \pm\sqrt{24}$
b. $q = \pm 2\sqrt{6}$
c. $q = -14\sqrt{6}$ or $q = 10\sqrt{6}$
d. $q = -12 \pm 2\sqrt{6}$
e. none of these

59. Solve for l: $P = \pi l^2 r$

a. $l = \pm\sqrt{\pi r P}$
b. $l = \pm\pi r P$
c. $l = \pm\sqrt{\dfrac{\pi}{Pr}}$
d. $l = \pm\sqrt{\dfrac{r}{\pi P}}$
e. none of these

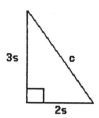

60. From the above right triangle, express s in terms of c (simplify your answer).

 a. $s = \dfrac{\sqrt{13}}{13}\, c$

 b. $s = \dfrac{\sqrt{5}}{5}\, c$

 c. $s = \dfrac{c}{5}$

 d. $s = \dfrac{c}{13}$

 e. none of these

61. What constant must be added to $m^2 - 14m$ to make a perfect square trinomial?

 a. 196
 b. 49
 c. −196
 d. −49
 e. none of these

62. What constant must be added to $y^2 - 6y$ to make a perfect square trinomial?

 a. 36
 b. −36
 c. 9
 d. −9
 e. none of these

63. What constant must be added to $y^2 - \dfrac{5}{4}y$ to make a perfect square trinomial?

 a. $\dfrac{25}{64}$

 b. $\dfrac{-25}{64}$

 c. $\dfrac{25}{16}$

 d. $\dfrac{-25}{16}$

 e. none of these

64. What constant must be added to $x^2 - \frac{7}{3}x$ to make a perfect square trinomial?

a. $\frac{49}{9}$

b. $\frac{-49}{9}$

c. $\frac{-49}{36}$

d. $\frac{49}{36}$

e. none of these

65. Write the following equation in standard form $ax^2 + bx + c = 0$, and identify a, b, and c:

$3x^2 = 9 - 2x$

a. $3x^2 - 9 + 2x = 0$, $a = 3$, $b = -9$, $c = 2$
b. $3x^2 + 9 - 2x = 0$, $a = 3$, $b = 9$, $c = -2$
c. $3x^2 - 2x - 9 = 0$, $a = 3$, $b = -2$, $c = -9$
d. $3x^2 - 2x + 9 = 0$, $a = 3$, $b = -2$, $c = 9$
e. none of these

66. When the following quadratic equation is written in standard form with $a > 0$, find a, b, and c:

$2x(x + 5) = 9$

a. $a = 2$, $b = 10$, $c = 9$
b. $a = 2$, $b = 5$, $c = 9$
c. $a = 2$, $b = 10$, $c = -9$
d. $a = 2$, $b = 0$, $c = 1$
e. none of these

67. When the following quadratic equation is written in standard form with $a > 0$, find a, b, and c:

$9x + 2 = x(5 - 3x)$

a. $a = 3$, $b = 4$, $c = 2$
b. $a = 3$, $b = 14$, $c = 2$
c. $a = 3$, $b = -4$, $c = -2$
d. $a = 3$, $b = -14$, $c = -2$
e. none of these

68. Use the quadratic formula to solve:

$$x^2 - x - 5 = 0$$

a. $x = -5$ or $x = 1$

b. $x = \dfrac{-1 \pm \sqrt{21}}{2}$

c. $x = \dfrac{-1 \pm \sqrt{19}}{2}$

d. $x = \dfrac{1 \pm \sqrt{19}}{2}$

e. none of these

69. Use the quadratic formula to solve:

$$x^2 - 5x + 1 = 0$$

a. $x = \dfrac{5 \pm \sqrt{21}}{2}$

b. $x = \dfrac{5 \pm \sqrt{29}}{2}$

c. $x = \dfrac{-5 \pm \sqrt{21}}{2}$

d. $x = \dfrac{-5 \pm \sqrt{29}}{2}$

e. none of the above

70. Use the quadratic formula to solve:

$$3y^2 - 7y - 2 = 0$$

a. $y = \dfrac{-7 \pm \sqrt{73}}{6}$

b. $y = \dfrac{7 \pm \sqrt{73}}{6}$

c. $y = -2$ or $y = -\dfrac{1}{3}$

d. $y = 2$ or $y = \dfrac{1}{3}$

e. none of these

259

71. Use the quadratic formula to solve (simplify your answer):

   $x^2 = 9x - 9$

   a. $\dfrac{-9 \pm 3\sqrt{13}}{2}$

   b. $\dfrac{9 \pm 3\sqrt{13}}{2}$

   c. $\dfrac{-9 \pm 3\sqrt{5}}{2}$

   d. $\dfrac{9 \pm 3\sqrt{5}}{2}$

   e. none of these

72. Use the quadratic formula to solve (simplify your answer):

   $x^2 = 7x - 1$

   a. $5\sqrt{5}$ or $2\sqrt{5}$

   b. $\dfrac{-7 \pm \sqrt{53}}{2}$

   c. $\dfrac{7 \pm \sqrt{53}}{2}$

   d. $\dfrac{-7 \pm 3\sqrt{5}}{2}$

   e. none of these

73. Use the quadratic formula to solve (simplify your answer):

   $t^2 = 4t + 8$

   a. $2 \pm 2\sqrt{3}$

   b. $2 \pm 4\sqrt{3}$

   c. $4 \pm 2\sqrt{3}$

   d. $\pm 4\sqrt{3}$

   e. none of these

74. Use the quadratic formula to solve (simplify your answer):

$$2y^2 = 6y + 1$$

a. $\dfrac{-3 \pm \sqrt{7}}{2}$

b. $\dfrac{3 \pm \sqrt{7}}{2}$

c. $\dfrac{-3 \pm \sqrt{11}}{2}$

d. $\dfrac{3 \pm \sqrt{11}}{2}$

e. none of these

75. Use the quadratic formula to solve (simplify your answer):

$$5x^2 = 2x + 2$$

a. $\dfrac{1 \pm 2\sqrt{11}}{5}$

b. $1 \pm \sqrt{11}$

c. $\dfrac{\pm 2\sqrt{11}}{5}$

d. $\dfrac{-1 \pm \sqrt{11}}{5}$

e. none of these

76. Use any algebraic method to solve:

$$x(x - 3) = 10$$

a. $x = 0$ or $x = 3$
b. $x = 10$ or $x = 13$
c. $x = 2$ or $x = -5$
d. $x = -2$ or $x = 5$
e. none of these

77. Use any algebraic method to solve:

$$4y(2y + 1) = 180$$

a. $y = 45$ or $y = \dfrac{179}{2}$

b. $y = 0$ or $y = -\dfrac{1}{2}$

c. $y = -5$ or $y = 4\dfrac{1}{2}$

d. $y = \dfrac{4 \pm \sqrt{326}}{8}$

e. none of these

261

78. Use any appropriate algebraic method to solve:

$$y(y + 5) = 9$$

a. $y = 0$ or $y = -5$
b. $y = 9$ or $y = 4$

c. $y = \dfrac{5 \pm \sqrt{11}}{2}$

d. $y = \dfrac{-5 \pm \sqrt{61}}{2}$

e. none of these

79. Find all solutions, both real and complex, to:

$$m^2 = -9$$

a. $m = \pm 9i$
b. $m = \pm 3i$
c. $m = 1 \pm 9i$
d. $m = 1 \pm 3i$
e. none of these

80. Find all solutions, both real and complex, to:

$$x^2 + 3x + 11 = 0$$

a. $-\dfrac{3}{2} \pm \dfrac{\sqrt{53}}{2} i$

b. $\dfrac{3}{2} \pm \dfrac{\sqrt{53}}{2} i$

c. $-\dfrac{3}{2} \pm \dfrac{\sqrt{35}}{2} i$

d. $\dfrac{3}{2} \pm \dfrac{\sqrt{35}}{2} i$

e. none of these

81. Find all solutions, both real and complex, to:

$$y^2 + 5y + 10 = 0$$

a. $-\dfrac{5}{2} \pm \dfrac{\sqrt{15}}{2} i$

b. $\dfrac{5}{2} \pm \dfrac{\sqrt{15}}{2} i$

c. $-\dfrac{5}{2} \pm \dfrac{\sqrt{65}}{2} i$

d. $\dfrac{5}{2} \pm \dfrac{\sqrt{65}}{2} i$

e. none of these

82. Find all solutions, both real and complex, to:

   $x(x - 4) = -6$

   a. $2 \pm \sqrt{10}\,i$
   b. $2 \pm \sqrt{2}\,i$
   c. $2 \pm 2\sqrt{10}\,i$
   d. $2 \pm 2\sqrt{2}\,i$
   e. none of these

83. Given $ax^2 + bx + c = 0$, which of the following is true?

   a. if $b^2 + 4ac > 0$, there are two real roots
   b. if $b^2 - 4ac > 0$, there are two real roots
   c. if $b^2 - 4ac < 0$, there are two real roots
   d. if $b^2 + 4ac = 0$, there are two real roots
   e. none of these

84. Given $ax^2 + bx + c = 0$, which of the following is true?

   a. if $b - 4ac < 0$, there are two complex, non-real roots
   b. if $b + 4ac < 0$, there are two complex, non-real roots
   c. if $b - 4ac > 0$, there are two real roots
   d. if $b + 4ac > 0$, there are two real roots
   e. none of these

85. One number, x, is three times another number, y. Their product is 81. Find x and y.

   a. $x = 3\sqrt{3}$ and $y = -3\sqrt{3}$
   b. $x = 27$ and $y = 3$ or $x = -27$ and $y = -3$
   c. $x = 6\sqrt{3}$ and $y = 2\sqrt{3}$ or $x = -6\sqrt{3}$ and $y = -2\sqrt{3}$
   d. $x = 9\sqrt{3}$ and $y = 3\sqrt{3}$ or $x = -9\sqrt{3}$ and $y = -3\sqrt{3}$
   e. none of these

86. A car that was involved in an accident left skid marks measuring 420 feet. The braking distance d for this particular make of car can be approximated by $d = \frac{1}{10}v^2 + v$, where v is the speed of the car. What was the speed of the car at the time of the accident?

   a. 30 mph
   b. 40 mph
   c. 50 mph
   d. 60 mph
   e. none of these

87. If an object is dropped, the distance d dropped in terms of the speed v is $d = \frac{v^2}{64}$, where d is in feet and v is in feet per second. An object is dropped from an airplane flying at 4,000 feet. What is the speed of the object when it hits the ground?

   a.   25 feet per second
   b. $160\sqrt{2}$ feet per second
   c. $25\sqrt{2}$ feet per second
   d. $160\sqrt{10}$ feet per second
   e.   none of these

88. A manufacturing company makes and sells x fans each day. The daily cost C is given by $C = \frac{1}{5}x^2 + 625$ and the daily revenue R is given by R = 30x. The company cannot make more than 100 fans each day. Find the break-even point for the company.

   a.   100 fans each day
   b.   50 fans each day
   c.   35 fans each day
   d.   25 fans each day
   e.   none of these

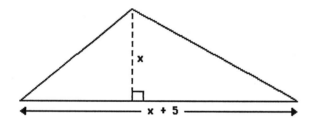

89. The base of a triangle is 5 cm more than its height (refer to the above diagram). If the area is $\frac{1}{2}$ square centimeters, find the length of the base.

   a. $\frac{1}{4}$ cm

   b. $\frac{5 + \sqrt{29}}{2}$ cm

   c. $\frac{1}{5}$ cm

   d. $\frac{5 + \sqrt{21}}{2}$ cm

   e.   none of these

264

90. An open box is to be made from a square sheet of cardboard by cutting squares measuring 5 cm on a side from each corner and folding up the sides. If the required volume is 75 cubic centimeters, what size cardboard is needed to make the box?

    a. 15 cm on each side
    b. $10 + 2\sqrt{15}$ cm on each side
    c. 25 cm on each side
    d. $10 + \sqrt{15}$ cm on each side
    e. none of these

91. Find the coordinates of the vertex for $y = (x - 9)^2$

    a. $(0, 9)$
    b. $(0, -9)$
    c. $(9, 0)$
    d. $(-9, 0)$
    e. none of these

92. Find the coordinates of the vertex for $y = 5(x + 3)^2 - 4$

    a. $(5, 4)$
    b. $(-3, 4)$
    c. $(-3, -4)$
    d. $(5, -4)$
    e. none of these

93. Find the coordinates of the vertex for $y = 9(x - 8)^2 + 2$

    a. $(8, 2)$
    b. $(9, 8)$
    c. $(9, 2)$
    d. $(8, 9)$
    e. none of these

94. Complete the square to put the following equation in the form $y = a(x - h)^2 + k$:

    $y = x^2 + 8x + 9$

    a. $y = (x + 8)^2 + 9$
    b. $y = (x + 8)^2 + 25$
    c. $y = (x + 4)^2 + 25$
    d. $y = (x + 4)^2 - 7$
    e. none of these

265

95. Complete the square to put the following equation in the form
$y = a(x - h)^2 + k$:

   $y = 2x^2 - 16x + 41$

   a. $y = 2(x - 4)^2 + 25$
   b. $y = 2(x - 8)^2 + 25$
   c. $y = 2(x - 4)^2 + 9$
   d. $y = 2(x - 8)^2 + 9$
   e. none of these

96. Find the vertex for $y = x^2 + 10x + 23$

   a. $(0, 23)$
   b. $(10, 2)$
   c. $(-5, 2)$
   d. $(5, 48)$
   e. none of these

97. Find the vertex for $y = -x^2 - 6x - 4$

   a. $(-3, 5)$
   b. $(6, -5)$
   c. $(3, -5)$
   d. $(-6, 5)$
   e. none of these

98. Find the vertex for $y = 3x^2 + 12x + 3$

   a. $(0, 3)$
   b. $(-6, 3)$
   c. $(-2, -9)$
   d. $(4, -2)$
   e. none of these

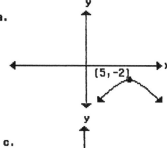
a.

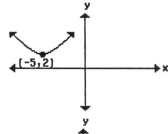
b.

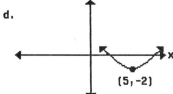

c.

d.

99. Which of the above is a graph of $y = -(x - 5)^2 + 2$?

    a. A
    b. B
    c. C
    d. D
    e. none of these

a.

b.

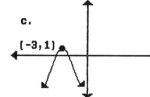
c.

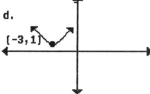
d.

100. Which of the above is a graph of $y = -(x - 3)^2 + 1$?

    a. A
    b. B
    c. C
    d. D
    e. none of these

1. TYPE:S DIFF:1 SECT:901 OBJ:901 RAND:Y

ANSWER:
$$w = \pm\frac{3}{4}$$

2. TYPE:S DIFF:2 SECT:901 OBJ:901 RAND:Y

ANSWER:
$$y = \pm\sqrt{35}$$

3. TYPE:S DIFF:3 SECT:901 OBJ:901 RAND:Y

ANSWER:
$$t = \pm 2\sqrt{6}$$

4. TYPE:S DIFF:1 SECT:901 OBJ:902 RAND:Y

ANSWER:
$$y = 1 \text{ or } y = -9$$

5. TYPE:S DIFF:3 SECT:901 OBJ:902 RAND:Y

ANSWER:
$$m = 3 \pm 4\sqrt{3}$$

6. TYPE:S DIFF:2 SECT:901 OBJ:902 RAND:Y

ANSWER:
$$q = -9 \pm \sqrt{14}$$

7. TYPE:S DIFF:2 SECT:901 OBJ:903 GRAPH FORMAT:G
   QUESTION GRAPH:1 RAND:Y

ANSWER:
$$s = \frac{\sqrt{26}}{26}\, c$$

8. TYPE:S DIFF:2 SECT:901 OBJ:903 RAND:Y

ANSWER:
$$y = \pm\sqrt{\frac{m}{\pi t}} = \frac{\pm\sqrt{m\pi t}}{\pi t}$$

268

9. ANS:**36** TYPE:**S** DIFF:**1** SECT:**902** OBJ:**904** RAND:**Y**

10. TYPE:**S** DIFF:**2** SECT:**902** OBJ:**904** RAND:**Y**

ANSWER:
$$\frac{9}{100}$$

11. TYPE:**S** DIFF:**1** SECT:**902** OBJ:**905** RAND:**Y**

ANSWER:
$$x = -5 \text{ or } x = 3$$

12. TYPE:**S** DIFF:**1** SECT:**902** OBJ:**905** RAND:**Y**

ANSWER:
$$y = -2 \text{ or } y = 8$$

13. TYPE:**S** DIFF:**2** SECT:**902** OBJ:**905** RAND:**Y**

ANSWER:
$$m = \frac{5 \pm \sqrt{13}}{2}$$

14. TYPE:**S** DIFF:**2** SECT:**902** OBJ:**905** RAND:**Y**

ANSWER:
$$r = \frac{9 \pm \sqrt{89}}{2}$$

15. TYPE:**S** DIFF:**3** SECT:**902** OBJ:**905** RAND:**Y**

ANSWER:
$$x = \frac{-5 \pm \sqrt{65}}{4}$$

16. TYPE:**S** DIFF:**3** SECT:**902** OBJ:**905** RAND:**Y**

ANSWER:
$$n = \frac{2 \pm \sqrt{10}}{3}$$

269

17. TYPE:**S** DIFF:**1** SECT:**903** OBJ:**906** RAND:**Y**

ANSWER:
$$5x^2 - 3x + 4 = 0$$
$$a = 5, \quad b = -3, \quad c = 4$$

18. TYPE:**S** DIFF:**2** SECT:**903** OBJ:**906** RAND:**Y**

ANSWER:
$$2x^2 - 3x + 4 = 0$$
$$a = 2, \quad b = -3, \quad c = 4$$

19. TYPE:**S** DIFF:**1** SECT:**903** OBJ:**907** RAND:**Y**

ANSWER:
$$x = \frac{3 \pm \sqrt{37}}{2}$$

20. TYPE:**S** DIFF:**1** SECT:**903** OBJ:**907** RAND:**Y**

ANSWER:
$$y = \frac{7 \pm \sqrt{57}}{2}$$

21. TYPE:**S** DIFF:**2** SECT:**903** OBJ:**907** RAND:**Y**

ANSWER:
$$\frac{3 \pm 3\sqrt{5}}{2}$$

22. TYPE:**S** DIFF:**2** SECT:**903** OBJ:**907** RAND:**Y**

ANSWER:
$$x = \frac{-7 \pm 3\sqrt{5}}{2}$$

23. TYPE:**S** DIFF:**3** SECT:**903** OBJ:**907** RAND:**Y**

ANSWER:
$$x = \frac{-3 \pm \sqrt{15}}{2}$$

24. TYPE:S DIFF:3 SECT:903 OBJ:907 RAND:Y

ANSWER:

$$x = \frac{3 \pm \sqrt{3}}{3}$$

25. TYPE:S DIFF:2 SECT:903 OBJ:908 RAND:Y

ANSWER:
    $x = -4$ or $x = 5$

26. TYPE:S DIFF:3 SECT:903 OBJ:908 RAND:Y

ANSWER:

$$x = \frac{9 \pm \sqrt{97}}{2}$$

27. TYPE:S DIFF:2 SECT:904 OBJ:909 RAND:Y

ANSWER:

$$y = -\frac{3}{2} \pm \frac{\sqrt{51}}{2} i$$

28. TYPE:S DIFF:2 SECT:904 OBJ:909 RAND:Y

ANSWER:

$$m = -\frac{5}{2} \pm \frac{\sqrt{23}}{2} i$$

29. TYPE:S DIFF:3 SECT:904 OBJ:909 RAND:Y

ANSWER:
    $x = 1 \pm \sqrt{5} i$

30. TYPE:S DIFF:2 SECT:904 OBJ:910 RAND:Y

ANSWER:
    2 complex roots

31. TYPE:S DIFF:2 SECT:904 OBJ:910 RAND:Y

ANSWER:
    2 real roots

271

32. TYPE:S DIFF:2 SECT:905 OBJ:911 RAND:Y

ANSWER:
   3, reciprocal $\frac{1}{3}$ or $-\frac{1}{3}$ reciprocal -3

33. TYPE:S DIFF:2 SECT:905 OBJ:911 RAND:Y

ANSWER:
   $\frac{4}{3}$, reciprocal $\frac{3}{4}$ or $-\frac{3}{4}$, reciprocal $-\frac{4}{3}$

34. TYPE:S DIFF:2 SECT:905 OBJ:911 RAND:Y

ANSWER:
   50 bowls each day

35. TYPE:S DIFF:1 SECT:905 OBJ:911 RAND:Y

ANSWER:
   $2\sqrt{3}$ and $6\sqrt{3}$ or $-2\sqrt{3}$ and $-6\sqrt{3}$

36. ANS:40 mph TYPE:S DIFF:2 SECT:905 OBJ:911 RAND:Y

37. TYPE:S DIFF:1 SECT:905 OBJ:911 RAND:Y

ANSWER:
   $160\sqrt{5}$ feet per second

38. TYPE:S DIFF:3 SECT:905 OBJ:911 GRAPH FORMAT:G
    QUESTION GRAPH:2 RAND:Y

ANSWER:
   height = $-1 + \sqrt{10}$ inches
   base = $1 + \sqrt{10}$ inches

39. TYPE:S DIFF:3 SECT:905 OBJ:911 RAND:Y

ANSWER:
   $8 + \sqrt{30}$ inches on each side

40. ANS:(5, 0) TYPE:S DIFF:1 SECT:906 OBJ:912 RAND:Y

41. ANS:(-2, -5) TYPE:S DIFF:2 SECT:906 OBJ:912 RAND:Y

42. ANS:(3, 4) TYPE:S DIFF:2 SECT:906 OBJ:912 RAND:Y

43. TYPE:S DIFF:1 SECT:906 OBJ:913 RAND:Y

ANSWER:
    $y = (x + 9)^2 - 3$

44. TYPE:S DIFF:2 SECT:906 OBJ:913 RAND:Y

ANSWER:
    $y = 3(x + 4)^2 - 8$

45. ANS:(-3, -2) TYPE:S DIFF:1 SECT:906 OBJ:914 RAND:Y

46. ANS:(4, 5) TYPE:S DIFF:2 SECT:906 OBJ:914 RAND:Y

47. ANS:(-5, 8) TYPE:S DIFF:1 SECT:906 OBJ:914 RAND:Y

48. ANS:(2, 4) TYPE:S DIFF:2 SECT:906 OBJ:914 RAND:Y

49. TYPE:S DIFF:2 SECT:906 OBJ:915 GRAPH FORMAT:G
    QUESTION GRAPH:3 ANSWER GRAPH:4 RAND:Y

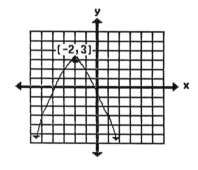

273

50. TYPE:S DIFF:3 SECT:906 OBJ:915 GRAPH FORMAT:G
    QUESTION GRAPH:5 ANSWER GRAPH:6 RAND:Y

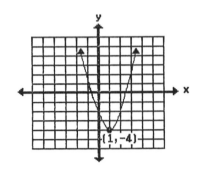

51. ANS:c TYPE:M DIFF:1 SECT:901 OBJ:901 RAND:Y

52. ANS:b TYPE:M DIFF:2 SECT:901 OBJ:901 RAND:Y

53. ANS:c TYPE:M DIFF:3 SECT:901 OBJ:901 RAND:Y

54. ANS:d TYPE:M DIFF:3 SECT:901 OBJ:901 RAND:Y

55. ANS:e TYPE:M DIFF:1 SECT:901 OBJ:902 RAND:Y

56. ANS:d TYPE:M DIFF:2 SECT:901 OBJ:902 RAND:Y

57. ANS:c TYPE:M DIFF:3 SECT:901 OBJ:902 RAND:Y

58. ANS:c TYPE:M DIFF:3 SECT:901 OBJ:902 RAND:Y

59. ANS:e TYPE:M DIFF:2 SECT:901 OBJ:903 RAND:Y

60. ANS:a TYPE:M DIFF:2 SECT:901 OBJ:903 GRAPH FORMAT:G
    QUESTION GRAPH:7 RAND:Y

61. ANS:b TYPE:M DIFF:1 SECT:902 OBJ:904 RAND:Y

62. ANS:c TYPE:M DIFF:1 SECT:902 OBJ:904 RAND:Y

63. ANS:a TYPE:M DIFF:2 SECT:902 OBJ:904 RAND:Y

```
64. ANS:d  TYPE:M  DIFF:2  SECT:902  OBJ:904  RAND:Y

65. ANS:e  TYPE:M  DIFF:1  SECT:903  OBJ:906  RAND:Y

66. ANS:c  TYPE:M  DIFF:1  SECT:903  OBJ:906  RAND:Y

67. ANS:a  TYPE:M  DIFF:2  SECT:903  OBJ:906  RAND:Y

68. ANS:e  TYPE:M  DIFF:1  SECT:903  OBJ:907  RAND:Y

69. ANS:a  TYPE:M  DIFF:1  SECT:903  OBJ:907  RAND:Y

70. ANS:b  TYPE:M  DIFF:1  SECT:903  OBJ:907  RAND:Y

71. ANS:d  TYPE:M  DIFF:2  SECT:903  OBJ:907  RAND:Y

72. ANS:e  TYPE:M  DIFF:2  SECT:903  OBJ:907  RAND:Y

73. ANS:a  TYPE:M  DIFF:3  SECT:903  OBJ:907  RAND:Y

74. ANS:d  TYPE:M  DIFF:3  SECT:903  OBJ:907  RAND:Y

75. ANS:e  TYPE:M  DIFF:3  SECT:903  OBJ:907  RAND:Y

76. ANS:d  TYPE:M  DIFF:2  SECT:903  OBJ:908  RAND:Y

77. ANS:c  TYPE:M  DIFF:3  SECT:903  OBJ:908  RAND:Y

78. ANS:d  TYPE:M  DIFF:3  SECT:903  OBJ:908  RAND:Y

79. ANS:b  TYPE:M  DIFF:1  SECT:904  OBJ:909  RAND:Y

80. ANS:c  TYPE:M  DIFF:2  SECT:904  OBJ:909  RAND:Y

81. ANS:a  TYPE:M  DIFF:2  SECT:904  OBJ:909  RAND:Y
```

82. ANS:b TYPE:M DIFF:3 SECT:904 OBJ:909 RAND:Y

83. ANS:b TYPE:M DIFF:2 SECT:904 OBJ:910 RAND:Y

84. ANS:e TYPE:M DIFF:2 SECT:904 OBJ:910 RAND:Y

85. ANS:d TYPE:M DIFF:1 SECT:905 OBJ:911 RAND:Y

86. ANS:d TYPE:M DIFF:2 SECT:905 OBJ:911 RAND:Y

87. ANS:d TYPE:M DIFF:1 SECT:905 OBJ:911 RAND:Y

88. ANS:d TYPE:M DIFF:2 SECT:905 OBJ:911 RAND:Y

89. ANS:b TYPE:M DIFF:3 SECT:905 OBJ:911 GRAPH FORMAT:G
    QUESTION GRAPH:8 RAND:Y

90. ANS:d TYPE:M DIFF:3 SECT:905 OBJ:911 RAND:Y

91. ANS:a TYPE:M DIFF:1 SECT:906 OBJ:912 RAND:Y

92. ANS:c TYPE:M DIFF:2 SECT:906 OBJ:912 RAND:Y

93. ANS:a TYPE:M DIFF:2 SECT:906 OBJ:912 RAND:Y

94. ANS:d TYPE:M DIFF:1 SECT:906 OBJ:913 RAND:Y

95. ANS:c TYPE:M DIFF:2 SECT:906 OBJ:913 RAND:Y

96. ANS:c TYPE:M DIFF:1 SECT:906 OBJ:914 RAND:Y

97. ANS:a TYPE:M DIFF:2 SECT:906 OBJ:914 RAND:Y

98. ANS:c TYPE:M DIFF:2 SECT:906 OBJ:914 RAND:Y

99. ANS:e TYPE:M DIFF:2 SECT:906 OBJ:915 GRAPH FORMAT:G
    QUESTION GRAPH:9 RAND:Y

100. ANS:**b** TYPE:**M** DIFF:**2** SECT:**906** OBJ:**915** GRAPH FORMAT:**G**
    QUESTION GRAPH:**10** RAND:**Y**

TestMaker III is an algorithm-based testing system that allows you to create an almost infinite number of customized tests. TestMaker combines open-ended questions whose numerical values can be manipulated to create a wide variety of questions for each objective with multiple choice questions for flexibility. TestMaker III allows you to:

1. Construct tests or drill exercises that focus on a specific learning objective.

2. Print several forms of the same chapter test with questions rearranged to discourage copying.

3. Print a similar chapter test with different numerical values to use as a make-up exam.

4. Create a test covering one or more chapters of the text.

5. Include subscripts, superscripts, special symbols, graphs, and number lines.

6. Save the test items in a data file.

The Computerized Test Bank comes with a User's Guide that contains this information in more detail. If you have additional questions about this software, please call your Saunders sales representative.

Show your answers on the Student Answer Sheet.

1. A triangle has two sides that are $\frac{3}{4}$ inches long and one side that is $\frac{7}{8}$ inches long. Find the distance around the triangle.

   A) $\frac{21}{12}$ inches   B) $\frac{13}{8}$ inches

   C) $\frac{13}{12}$ inches   D) $\frac{19}{8}$ inches

2. Write $4 + 2(5 + 3)$ in words.
   A) the quantity four plus two times the quantity five plus three
   B) four plus two plus the quantity five plus three
   C) four plus two times the quantity five plus three
   D) four plus two times five plus three

3. Which of the following numbers is less than -0.52?
   A) -0.53 B) -0.5
   C) -0.4 D) -0.51

4. Find the additive inverse of $\frac{3}{7}$.

   A) $-\frac{7}{3}$ B) $\frac{3}{7}$

   C) $-\frac{3}{7}$ D) $\frac{7}{3}$

5. Find 0 divided by -4.
   A) 0 B) 4
   C) not defined   D) -4

6. Which of the following is a solution of $x^2 - 15 = 2x$?
   A) 3 B) 5
   C) 6 D) 4

Show your answers on the Student Answer Sheet.

---

7. State the property that is illustrated.

    $-4(3 - 2) = (-4)(3) + (-4)(-2)$

    A) commutative property   B) associative property
    C) distributive property   D) additive identity property

8. Simplify the expression.

    $\frac{1}{2} + \frac{2}{3}(z - 3)$

    A) $\frac{2}{3}z - \frac{3}{2}$ B) $\frac{2}{3}z + \frac{3}{2}$

    C) $\frac{2}{3}z + \frac{3}{6}$ D) $\frac{2}{3}z - \frac{1}{6}$

9. Find the product.

    $\frac{7}{18} \cdot \frac{6}{5} \cdot \frac{8}{7}$

10. Find the quotient.

    $\frac{10}{9} \div \frac{6}{13}$

11. Find the sum.

    $\frac{2}{3} + \frac{7}{9}$

12. Find the difference.

    $\frac{2}{7} - \frac{2}{9}$

13. Simplify the expression.

    $\left[(8 - 4)^2 - 4\right] \div 2$

14. Simplify the expression.

    $(9 + 6) \div (9 - 8)$

15. Graph the numbers from the set on the number line.

    $\{-4, 5, 3.5, 0.8, \sqrt{8}\}$

16. Use < or > to make a true statement.

    2.34 _____ 2.35

Show your answers on the Student Answer Sheet.

---

17. Find the absolute value of $-\frac{7}{6}$.

18. Subtract 12 from −18.

19. Simplify the expression.

    $|2 - 7| - |3 - 6|$

20. Simplify the expression.

    $(0.9)(-4.3)$

21. Find the reciprocal of $-\frac{7}{3}$.

22. Find the quotient.

    $-\frac{7}{3} \div \left(-\frac{3}{2}\right)$

23. Evaluate $-3fg - 6fh - 5gh$ when $f = 4$, $g = -2$, $h = -5$.

24. Write the sentence as an equation using n as a variable.
    Four times the square of a number is 220.

25. Simplify the expression.

    $6 - (x + 5) + 5$

Student Name _____ Score_____

Student Answer Sheet - Show all work. Use extra sheets if necessary.

[1]_____

[2]_____

[3]_____

[4]_____

[5]_____

[6]_____

[7]_____

[8]_____

[9]_____

[10]_____

Student Name _____ Score_____

Student Answer Sheet - Show all work. Use extra sheets if necessary.

[11]_____

[12]_____

[13]_____

[14]_____

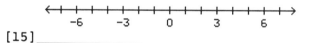

[15]_____

[16]_____

[17]_____

[18]_____

[19]_____

Student Name _____ Score_____

Student Answer Sheet - Show all work. Use extra sheets if necessary.

[20]_____

[21]_____

[22]_____

[23]_____

[24]_____

[25]_____

_____

Key Sheet
_____

D
[1] _____

C
[2] _____

A
[3] _____

C
[4] _____

A
[5] _____

B
[6] _____

C
[7] _____

A
[8] _____

$\frac{8}{15}$
[9] _____

$\frac{65}{27}$
[10] _____

Key Sheet

[11] $\frac{13}{9}$

[12] $\frac{4}{63}$

[13] 6

[14] 15

[15]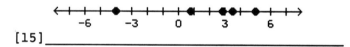

[16] <

[17] $\frac{7}{6}$

[18] -30

[19] 2

Key Sheet

---

[20] -3.87

[21] $-\dfrac{3}{7}$

[22] $\dfrac{14}{9}$

[23] 94

[24] $4n^2 = 220$

[25] $6 - x$

Show your answers on the Student Answer Sheet.

1. Write the word phrase as a simplified algebraic expression.

   three plus two times the sum of n and −8

   A) 2n − 13   B) 5n − 8
   C) 2n + 19   D) 3 + 2(n + (−8))

2. Solve the equation.

   9 − (a − 3) = 4(1 − a)

   A) $-\dfrac{3}{8}$ B) $-\dfrac{8}{3}$

   C) $-\dfrac{3}{2}$ D) $\dfrac{2}{3}$

3. Convert the word phrase into an algebraic expression.

   ten fewer than thirty-four percent of a number

   A) 0.34x − 10   B) 34x − 10
   C) 10 − 34x   D) 10 − 0.34x

4. The sum of two numbers is 53. The smaller number is seven less than one-half the larger number. Find the larger number.

   A) 33   B) 20
   C) 13   D) 40

5. Solve the equation.

   $1 - \dfrac{1}{3}a = \dfrac{2}{3} + \dfrac{2}{5}a$

   A) $\dfrac{11}{5}$ B) $\dfrac{5}{11}$

   C) $\dfrac{1}{5}$ D) $-\dfrac{1}{5}$

Show your answers on the Student Answer Sheet.

---

6. Solve the inequality.

$3x - 5 < 5x + 8$

A) $x < \frac{13}{2}$

B) $x < \frac{3}{2}$

C) $x > -\frac{13}{2}$

D) $x > \frac{3}{2}$

7. One angle of a triangle has a measure of 82 degrees. The measure of the second angle is two degrees greater than the measure of the third angle. Find the measure of the third angle.

A) 48 degrees

B) 50 degrees

C) 52 degrees

D) 46 degrees

8. Solve the equation for x.

$y - 1 = 2(x - 5)$

A) $x = \frac{y - 13}{2}$

B) $x = \frac{y + 9}{2}$

C) $y = 2x - 7$

D) $x = \frac{2}{y + 7}$

9. Simplify by combining like terms.

$-5(4 - 7xy^2) - (4 + 8xy^2) + 4xy^2$

10. Solve the equation.

$x - 3.1 = 7.9$

11. Solve the equation.

$5\frac{1}{6} + x = 6\frac{3}{7}$

12. Solve the equation.

$16 - 5x = 21 + 3x$

13. Solve the equation.

$-3x = 15$

14. Solve the equation.

$\frac{2}{3}x = 16$

Show your answers on the Student Answer Sheet.

15. Solve the equation.

    $-4x - 3 = -9$

16. Solve the equation.

    $3 - 5x = 7(x + 2)$

17. Convert the word phrase into an algebraic expression using x as a variable.

    the reciprocal of the sum of a number and sixteen

18. A number subtracted from $5\frac{3}{4}$ is $1\frac{3}{5}$. Find the number.

19. Write as a mathematical expression.

    the number of inches in s feet

20. Sportscenter is selling jogging shoes at 35% off. If the sale price is $39.80, what was the original price?

21. Tammy has $3.75 in dimes and quarters. If the number of quarters is 3 more than twice the number of dimes, how many of each coin does she have?

22. Solve the inequality and graph the solution.

    $c + 3 \le 9$

23. Solve the inequality and graph the solution.

    $-5 < x - 3 \le 3$

24. Solve the inequality.

    $3(3 - x) + 5 > 5$

25. How much interest is earned on $9000 invested at 7 percent for $6\frac{1}{2}$ years?

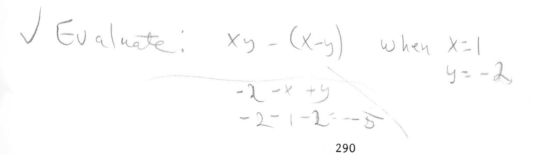

290

9

Student Name _____ Score_____

Student Answer Sheet - Show all work. Use extra sheets if necessary.

[1]_____

[2]_____

[3]_____

[4]_____

[5]_____

[6]_____

[7]_____

[8]_____

[9]_____

[10]_____

Student Name _____ Score_____

Student Answer Sheet — Show all work. Use extra sheets if necessary.

[11]_____

[12]_____

[13]_____

[14]_____

[15]_____

[16]_____

[17]_____

[18]_____

[19]_____

Student Name _____ Score_____

Student Answer Sheet - Show all work. Use extra sheets if necessary.

[20]_____

[21]_____

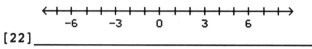

[22]_____

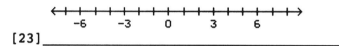

[23]_____

[24]_____

[25]_____

Key Sheet

[1] ___A_____

[2] ___B_____

[3] ___A_____

[4] ___D_____

[5] ___B_____

[6] ___C_____

[7] ___A_____

[8] ___B_____

[9] ___$31xy^2 - 24$_____

[10] ___$x = 11$_____

Key Sheet

---

[11] $x = 1\frac{11}{42}$

[12] $x = -\frac{5}{8}$

[13] -5

[14] 24

[15] $x = \frac{3}{2}$

[16] $x = -\frac{11}{12}$

[17] $\frac{1}{x + 16}$

[18] $4\frac{3}{20}$

[19] $12s$

Key Sheet

---

[20] $61.23

[21] 5 dimes and 13 quarters

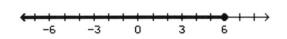

[22] Answer: c ≤ 6

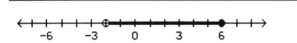

[23] Answer: −2 < x ≤ 6

[24] x < 3

[25] $4095.00

Show your answers on the Student Answer Sheet.

---

1. Simplify $(5^2)^0$.

    A) $\frac{1}{25}$ B) 25

    C) 5   D) 1

2. Evaluate and write the result in scientific notation.

    $(0.000009)(22,000,000)(0.002)$

    A) 3.96×10^{-1} B) 3.96×10^{2}

    C) 3.96×10^{-2} D) 3.96×10^{0}

3. Simplify.

    $$\frac{-1.2(x^2yz)^4}{0.3(xy)^3(x^2z^3)^2}$$

    A) $-\dfrac{4x^5y}{z^2}$ B) $-\dfrac{4xy}{z^2}$

    C) $\dfrac{4x^5y}{z^2}$ D) $\dfrac{4xy}{z^2}$

4. Which of the following is a polynomial of degree 3?

    A) $3x^2$ B) $-5 + 2x^3$

    C) $7x^2 + 2x - 1$ D) $x + y + z$

5. Subtract the sum $(2x^2 - 7x + 5) + (4x^2 + 8x - 3)$ from $10x^2 - x + 3$.

    A) $16x^2 + 2x + 5$ B) $4x^2 + 1$

    C) $4x^2 + 14x + 5$ D) $4x^2 - 2x + 1$

Show your answers on the Student Answer Sheet.

6. Multiply and simplify.

$(2x - 3)(3x + 5) - 2x(x - 5)$

A) $4x^2 - 9x - 15$ B) $4x^2 + 29x - 15$
C) $4x^2 + x - 15$ D) $4x^2 + 11x - 15$

7. Multiply.

$(x^3 + y^2)^2$

A) $x^6 + x^3y^2 + y^4$ B) $x^6 + 2xy + y^4$
C) $x^6 + y^4$ D) $x^6 + 2x^3y^2 + y^4$

8. Divide $6n^3 + 4n^2 - 8n$ by $2n$.

A) $3n^2 + 2n + 4$ B) $6n^2 + 4n - 8$
C) $3n^3 + 2n^2 - 4n$ D) $3n^2 + 2n - 4$

9. Simplify.

$(-5f^5g^2)^3$

10. Evaluate $(-x)^3$ for $x = \frac{5}{3}$.

11. Simplify without negative exponents.

$(jk^4)^2(j^2m^{-5})^2$

12. Write 0.00034 in scientific notation.

13. Multiply $-\frac{5}{4}p^5q^3$ by $p^6q^2r^5$.

14. Divide $12x^2yz^6$ by $4xy^6z^2$.

15. Simplify and write the polynomial in descending order of the
    exponents.

$3 - 4x - 4x^3 + 4x^4 - 7x^3$

16. Evaluate $-9s^3 - 6s^2 + 9$ for $s = 3$.

Show your answers on the Student Answer Sheet.

---

17. Add and write the answer in descending order of the exponents.

    $(-5s^3 + 3s - 4) + (-9s^4 + 8s + 9)$

18. Add and write the answer in descending order of the exponents.

    $(-7j^2 - 6j^4) - (-8j^3 + 7j^4) + (9j - 4j^2)$

19. Multiply.

    $(5m - 3)(6m - 5)$

    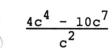

20. Multiply.

    $(a - 7)(2a^2 + 3a + 2)$

21. Multiply.

    $\left(3s^3 + \frac{2}{5}\right)^2$

22. Multiply.

    $(5x - 9y)(5x + 9y)$

23. Divide and simplify the answer.

    $\dfrac{4c^4 - 10c^7}{c^2}$

24. Divide.

    $(x^3 - 8x^2 + 13x - 6) \div (x - 1)$

25. Divide.

    $(x^4 + 4x^2 + 4x - 4) \div (x + 3)$

Student Name _____ Score_____

Student Answer Sheet - Show all work. Use extra sheets if necessary.

[1]_____

[2]_____

[3]_____

[4]_____

[5]_____

[6]_____

[7]_____

[8]_____

[9]_____

[10]_____

Student Name _____ Score_____

Student Answer Sheet - Show all work. Use extra sheets if necessary.

[11]_____

[12]_____

[13]_____

[14]_____

[15]_____

[16]_____

[17]_____

[18]_____

[19]_____

Student Name _____ Score_____

Student Answer Sheet - Show all work. Use extra sheets if necessary.

[20]_____

[21]_____

[22]_____

[23]_____

[24]_____

[25]_____

Key Sheet

---

[1] $\qquad$ D $\qquad$

[2] $\qquad$ A $\qquad$

[3] $\qquad$ B $\qquad$

[4] $\qquad$ B $\qquad$

[5] $\qquad$ D $\qquad$

[6] $\qquad$ D $\qquad$

[7] $\qquad$ D $\qquad$

[8] $\qquad$ D $\qquad$

[9] $\qquad$ $-125f^{15}g^6$ $\qquad$

[10] $\qquad$ $-\dfrac{125}{27}$ $\qquad$

Key Sheet

[11] $\dfrac{j^6 k^8}{m^{10}}$

[12] 3.4×10^{-4}

[13] $-\dfrac{5}{4} p^{11} q^5 r^5$

[14] $\dfrac{3 x z^4}{y^5}$

[15] $4x^4 - 11x^3 - 4x + 3$

[16] -288

[17] $-9s^4 - 5s^3 + 11s + 5$

[18] $-13j^4 + 8j^3 - 11j^2 + 9j$

[19] $30m^2 - 43m + 15$

_____

                              Key Sheet
_____

[20] $\underline{2a^3 - 11a^2 - 19a - 14 \qquad\qquad\qquad\qquad}$

[21] $\underline{9s^6 \ \mathbf{I} \ \frac{12}{5}s^3 \ \mathbf{I} \ \frac{4}{25} \qquad\qquad\qquad\qquad}$

[22] $\underline{25x^2 - 81y^2 \qquad\qquad\qquad\qquad\qquad}$

[23] $\underline{4c^2 - 10c^5 \qquad\qquad\qquad\qquad\qquad}$

[24] $\underline{x^2 - 7x + 6 \qquad\qquad\qquad\qquad\qquad}$

[25] $\underline{x^3 - 3x^2 + 13x - 35 + \frac{101}{x + 3} \qquad\qquad}$

Show your answers on the Student Answer Sheet.

1. Which of the following is NOT a prime number?

   A) 61   B) 91
   C) 97   D) 47

2. Factor completely.

   $a^2 - a - 12$

   A) $(a - 3)(a - 4)$ B) $(a - 6)(a + 2)$
   C) $(a - 6)(a - 2)$ D) $(a - 4)(a + 3)$

3. Which pair of factors gives the product $6x^2 + x - 15$?

   A) $(6x - 5)$ and $(x + 1)$ B) $(x + 5)$ and $(6x - 1)$
   C) $(3x - 5)$ and $(2x + 3)$ D) $(3x + 5)$ and $(2x - 3)$

4. Which of the following is a perfect square?

   A) $x^2 - xy + y^2$ B) $x^2 - 2xy + y^2$
   C) $x^2 - y^2$ D) $x^2 + xy + y^2$

5. Factor completely.

   $3c^4d^4 + 21c^3d^3 + 18c^2d^2$

   A) $c^2d^2(3c^2 + 21cd + 18)$ B) $3c^2d^2(c + 6)(c + 1)$
   C) $3c^2d^2(cd + 1)(cd + 6)$ D) $3c^2d^2(c^2 + 6cd + 7)$

6. Factor completely.

   $8x^3 - 1$

   A) $(2x - 1)(4x^2 + 1)$ B) $(2x - 1)(2x - 1)(2x - 1)$
   C) $(2x - 1)(4x^2 + 2x + 1)$ D) $(2x - 1)(4x^2 - 2x + 1)$

Show your answers on the Student Answer Sheet.

---

7. Solve for x.

    $x^3 - 2x^2 = 15x$

    A) -5, 3   B) -3, 0, 5
    C) -5, 0, 3   D) -3, 5

8. The length of the hypotenuse of a right triangle is 3 cm greater than twice the length of the shorter leg. The length of the other leg is 7 cm longer than the shorter leg. Find the length of the shorter leg.

    A) 6 cm   B) 5 cm
    C) 12 cm   D) 7 cm

9. Factor 378 into primes.

10. Find the missing factor.

    $-12x^8 = 4x^2(?)$

11. Factor out the greatest common factor.

    $18a^2 + 90a + 45$

12. Factor out the greatest common factor.

    $16s^5 - 8s^3 - 4s$

13. Factor completely.

    $m^2 + 11m + 24$

14. Factor completely.

    $c^2 - 9c + 14$

15. Factor completely.

    $32x^2 + 100x + 63$

16. Factor completely.

    $28m^2 - 47m - 36$

17. Factor completely.

    $m^2 - 9$

Show your answers on the Student Answer Sheet.

18. Factor completely.

$25f^2 - \dfrac{4}{9}$

19. Factor completely.

$81x^2 - 36xy + 4y^2$

20. Factor completely.

$2f^3 + 16$

21. Factor by grouping.

$x^3 + x^2 - 4x - 4$

22. Solve for x.

$(2x + 3)(x + 4) = 0$

23. Solve for m.

$m^2 + 13m + 36 = 0$

24. The sum of two numbers is 28 and their product is 195. Find the two numbers.

25. The length of a rectangle is 10 inches more than one-fourth its width. If the area is 156 square inches, find the length of the rectangle.

Student Name _____ Score_____

Student Answer Sheet - Show all work. Use extra sheets if necessary.

[1]_____

[2]_____

[3]_____

[4]_____

[5]_____

[6]_____

[7]_____

[8]_____

[9]_____

[10]_____

Student Name _____ Score_____

Student Answer Sheet – Show all work. Use extra sheets if necessary.

[11]_____

[12]_____

[13]_____

[14]_____

[15]_____

[16]_____

[17]_____

[18]_____

[19]_____

Student Name _____ Score_____

Student Answer Sheet - Show all work. Use extra sheets if necessary.

[20]_____

[21]_____

[22]_____

[23]_____

[24]_____

[25]_____

Key Sheet

[1]   B
_____

[2]   D
_____

[3]   D
_____

[4]   B
_____

[5]   C
_____

[6]   C
_____

[7]   B
_____

[8]   B
_____

[9] $2 \cdot 3^3 \cdot 7$
_____

[10] $-3x^6$
_____

Key Sheet

[11] $9(2a^2 + 10a + 5)$

[12] $4s(4s^4 - 2s^2 - 1)$

[13] $(m + 8)(m + 3)$

[14] $(c - 2)(c - 7)$

[15] $(4x + 9)(8x + 7)$

[16] $(7m + 4)(4m - 9)$

[17] $(m + 3)(m - 3)$

[18] $\left(5f - \frac{2}{3}\right)\left(5f + \frac{2}{3}\right)$

[19] $(9x - 2y)^2$

313

Key Sheet
---

[20] $2(f + 2)(f^2 - 2f + 4)$

[21] $(x + 1)(x + 2)(x - 2)$

[22] $x = -\dfrac{3}{2}$ or $x = -4$

[23] $m = -9$ or $m = -4$

[24] 15 and 13

[25] 13 inches

Show your answers on the Student Answer Sheet.

---

1. Reduce $\dfrac{-2x + 7}{2x^2 - 5x - 7}$ to lowest terms.

    A) $-\dfrac{1}{2x - 7}$ B) $\dfrac{1}{x + 1}$

    C) $-\dfrac{1}{x + 1}$ D) $\dfrac{1}{2x + 7}$

2. Find $\dfrac{x^2 + 8x + 15}{x^2 - 25}$ divided by $\dfrac{x + 3}{x - 5}$ in lowest terms.

    A) $\dfrac{1}{x - 5}$ B) $\dfrac{1}{x + 3}$

    C) $\dfrac{(x + 3)^2}{(x - 5)^2}$ D) 1

3. Find the least common denominator for $x + 5$ and $\dfrac{3}{5x}$.

    A) $5x(x + 5)$ B) $5x$
    C) $x + 5$ D) $15x(x + 5)$

4. Find the missing numerator.

    $$\dfrac{3a}{4(1 - a)} = \dfrac{?}{12(a - 1)}$$

    A) $-9a$ B) 9
    C) $9a$ D) -9

5. Find the sum in lowest terms.

    $$\dfrac{p^2 + 7p}{p^2 + 5p + 6} + \dfrac{p + 15}{p + 6}$$

    A) $\dfrac{p + 5}{p + 2}$ B) $\dfrac{p^2 + 8p + 15}{p^2 + 5p + 6}$

    C) $\dfrac{p + 5}{p^2 + 5p + 6}$ D) $\dfrac{p + 3}{p + 2}$

Show your answers on the Student Answer Sheet.

---

6. It took Jamie the same time to drive 300 miles as it did Jerry to drive 270 miles. Jerry's speed was 5 miles per hour less than Jamie's speed. How fast did Jamie drive?

    A) 45 mph   B) 55 mph
    C) 40 mph   D) 50 mph

7. The sum of two numbers is 18 and the sum of their reciprocals is $\frac{1}{4}$. Find the larger of the two numbers.

    A) 12   B) 10
    C) 14   D) 16

8. Suppose x varies inversely as the square of y and x = 15 when $y = \frac{2}{3}$. Find x when y = 5.

    A) $\frac{225}{2}$ B) $\frac{500}{3}$

    C) $\frac{20}{27}$ D) $\frac{4}{15}$

9. For what values of a, if any, is the rational expression undefined?

    $$\frac{a + 2}{a^2 - 6a + 8}$$

10. Write the rational expression in lowest terms.

    $$\frac{12m^4n^5}{10m^6n^4}$$

11. Write the rational expression in lowest terms.

    $$\frac{6 - 2a}{a^2 + 6a - 27}$$

12. Multiply and write the answer in lowest terms.

    $$\frac{6p}{7q} \cdot \frac{49q^4}{5p^3}$$

13. Multiply and write the answer in lowest terms.

    $$\frac{s^2 + 6s}{5s + 30} \cdot \frac{2s^2 - 2s}{6s - 6}$$

Show your answers on the Student Answer Sheet.

---

14. Divide and write the answer in lowest terms.

$$\frac{48j^4}{8k^4} \div \frac{6j^3}{32k^5}$$

15. Divide and write the answer in lowest terms.

$$\frac{m^2 - 49}{m - 8} \div \frac{m - 7}{m^2 - 64}$$

16. Find the least common denominator for the rational expressions.

$$\frac{9}{7f^5} \text{ and } \frac{14}{5f^2}$$

17. Find the least common denominator for the rational expressions.

$$\frac{8}{3s^2}, \frac{2}{3s + 1}, \text{ and } \frac{5}{3s}$$

18. Add and write the answer in lowest terms.

$$\frac{3f}{(3f + 2)(f + 1)} + \frac{2}{(3f + 2)(f + 1)}$$

19. Subtract and write the answer in lowest terms.

$$\frac{p + 3}{p^2 - 9} - \frac{p + 3}{p^2 - 2p - 15}$$

20. Simplify the complex fraction.

$$\frac{\frac{2}{7}}{\frac{12}{35}}$$

21. Simplify the complex fraction.

$$\frac{\frac{2}{c} + \frac{1}{18}}{\frac{3}{6c^2} - \frac{5}{c}}$$

22. Solve the equation.

$$\frac{3x + 1}{3} + \frac{3}{2} = \frac{7}{6}$$

Show your answers on the Student Answer Sheet.

23. Using the total resistance formula $\frac{1}{R} = \frac{1}{R_1} + \frac{1}{R_2}$, find the total resistance if $R_1 = 1\frac{5}{7}$ ohms and $R_2 = 12$ ohms.

24. It takes Juan 4 hours to mow a lawn using a power mower and it takes Oscar 7 hours to mow the same lawn using a hand mower. How long will it take them to mow the lawn if they work together?

25. Suppose g varies directly as f, and g = 30 when f = $\frac{5}{7}$.

    Find g when f = 8.

Student Name _____ Score_____

Student Answer Sheet - Show all work. Use extra sheets if necessary.

[1]_____

[2]_____

[3]_____

[4]_____

[5]_____

[6]_____

[7]_____

[8]_____

[9]_____

[10]_____

Student Name _____ Score_____

Student Answer Sheet – Show all work. Use extra sheets if necessary.

[11]_____

[12]_____

[13]_____

[14]_____

[15]_____

[16]_____

[17]_____

[18]_____

[19]_____

Student Name _____ Score_____

Student Answer Sheet – Show all work. Use extra sheets if necessary.

[20]_____

[21]_____

[22]_____

[23]_____

[24]_____

[25]_____

Key Sheet

[1] $\dfrac{C}{\rule{6cm}{0.4pt}}$

[2] $\dfrac{D}{\rule{6cm}{0.4pt}}$

[3] $\dfrac{B}{\rule{6cm}{0.4pt}}$

[4] $\dfrac{A}{\rule{6cm}{0.4pt}}$

[5] $\dfrac{A}{\rule{6cm}{0.4pt}}$

[6] $\dfrac{D}{\rule{6cm}{0.4pt}}$

[7] $\dfrac{A}{\rule{6cm}{0.4pt}}$

[8] $\dfrac{D}{\rule{6cm}{0.4pt}}$

[9] $\dfrac{2 \text{ and } 4}{\rule{6cm}{0.4pt}}$

[10] $\dfrac{\frac{6n}{5m^2}}{\rule{6cm}{0.4pt}}$

Key Sheet

---

[11] $-\dfrac{2}{a + 9}$

[12] $\dfrac{42q^3}{5p^2}$

[13] $\dfrac{s^2}{15}$

[14] $32jk$

[15] $(m + 7)(m + 8)$

[16] $35f^5$

[17] $3s^2(3s + 1)$

[18] $\dfrac{1}{f + 1}$

[19] $\dfrac{-2p - 6}{(p + 3)(p - 3)(p - 5)}$

Key Sheet

---

[20] $\dfrac{5}{6}$

[21] $\dfrac{36c + c^2}{9 - 90c}$

[22] $-\dfrac{2}{3}$

[23] $1\frac{1}{2}$ ohms

[24] $2\frac{6}{11}$ hours

[25] 336

Show your answers on the Student Answer Sheet.

---

1. Determine where in the coordinate plane the point (0, -4.5) would be located.

    A) on the x-axis   B) on the y-axis
    C) in quadrant III   D) in quadrant II

2. Which of the following ordered pairs is a solution of the equation $2x - 7y = 20$?

    A) (3, 2)   B) (4, -2)
    C) (14, 1)   D) (3, -2)

3. Find the slope, if it exists, of the line through the points (-13, 50) and (12, 50).

    A) undefined   B) 5
    C) 0   D) $\frac{1}{5}$

4. Find the equation for the line with slope 0 and y-intercept -0.2.

    A) $y = x - 0.2$ B) $y = -x - 0.2$
    C) $x = -0.2$ D) $y = -0.2$

5. Find the equation for the line that passes through the point (0.3, 0.6) and has slope -0.5.

    A) $y = -0.5x - 0.6$ B) $y = -0.5x + 0.75$
    C) $y = 0.5x + 0.6$ D) $y = 0.5x - 0.75$

6. Find the inequality that describes the following: Three times the y value exceeds the x value by 4.

    A) $x - 3y > 4$ B) $x + 3y > 4$
    C) $x - 3y < -4$ D) $x + 3y < 4$

7. Which of the following describes the third quadrant?

    A) $x < 0$ and $y < 0$ B) $x < 0$ and $y > 0$
    C) $x > 0$ and $y < 0$ D) $x > 0$ and $y > 0$

Show your answers on the Student Answer Sheet.

---

8. Woodworks Inc. makes desk sets and has a fixed cost of $75 and a variable cost of $15. If the company makes n sets each day, express the daily total cost C in terms of n.

A) C = 90n   B) C = 75n – 15
C) C = 75n + 15   D) C = 15n + 75

9. Find the ordered pair for the point A.

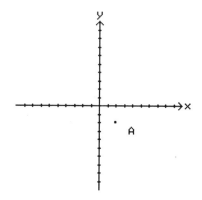

10. In which quadrant does the point (4, 2) lie?

11. Find the ordered pair that is a solution of 4x + y = –14 when y = 3.

12. Complete the table for the equation 2x + 4y = 9.

x	0		–5	
y		0		3

13. Draw the graph of x + y = 3.

14. Draw the graph of 5x + 4y = 20.

15. Draw the graph of y = 2.

16. Draw the graph of x – 9 = –3.

Show your answers on the Student Answer Sheet.

---

17. Find the slope of the given line.

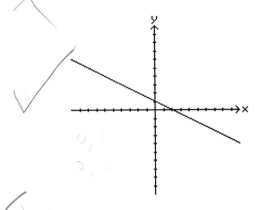

18. Find the slope of a line passing through the points (-2, -2) and (-3, -4).

19. Determine if the line through the points (9, 9) and (-2, 8) is parallel to the line through the points (-2, -5) and (4, -9).

20. Find the slope and the y-intercept of the line 9x + 4y = 10.

21. Using the slope-intercept form, find the equation of the line with the slope $-\frac{1}{5}$ and y-intercept 2.

22. Use the point-slope form to find the equation of the line through the points (-8, 4) and (-4, 3). Write the answer in the form ax + by = c.

23. Graph the inequality 4x + 2y < 8.

24. Graph the inequality 2y ≥ -2x.

25. Proline Corporation manufactures aluminum tennis rackets and graphite tennis rackets. Each aluminum racket costs $23 to make and each graphite racket costs $38 to make. The combined cost of making x aluminum rackets and y graphite rackets cannot exceed $76,000. Express this restriction by a linear inequality.

26. When the supply of California grapefruits on the East coast was 55 thousand flats, the price was $4.30 per flat. When the demand rose to 75 thousand flats, the price was $6.70 per flat. Assume that the price p per flat is linearly dependent upon the demand x (in thousands of flats). What is the price of grapefruits if the demand is 85 thousand flats?

Student Name _____ Score_____

Student Answer Sheet – Show all work. Use extra sheets if necessary.

[1]_____

[2]_____

[3]_____

[4]_____

[5]_____

[6]_____

[7]_____

[8]_____

[9]_____

[10]_____

Student Name _____ Score_____

Student Answer Sheet - Show all work. Use extra sheets if necessary.

[11]_____

x	0		−5	
y		0		3

[12]_____

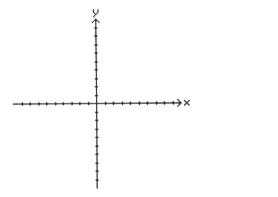

[13]_____

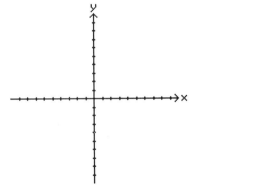

[14]_____

Chapter 6 – Linear Equations and Their Graphs   Form A-A

                        Student Name _____ Score_____

        Student Answer Sheet – Show all work. Use extra sheets if necessary.

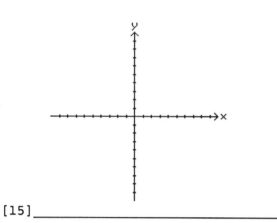

[15]_____

[16]_____

[17]_____

[18]_____

[19]_____

Student Name _____ Score_____

Student Answer Sheet – Show all work.   Use extra sheets if necessary.

[20]_____

[21]_____

[22]_____

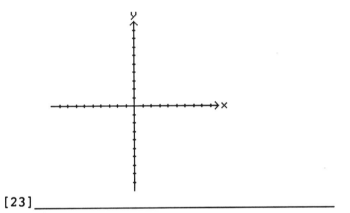

[23]_____

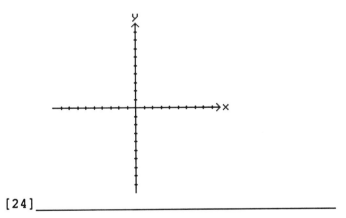

[24]_____

Student Name _____ Score_____

Student Answer Sheet - Show all work. Use extra sheets if necessary.

[25]_____

[26]_____

Key Sheet

---

[1]   B

[2]   D

[3]   C

[4]   D

[5]   B

[6]   C

[7]   A

[8]   D

[9]   (2, -2)

[10]   quadrant I

Key Sheet

[11] $\left(-\dfrac{17}{4},\ 3\right)$

x	0	9/2	−5	−3/2
y	9/4	0	19/4	3

[12]

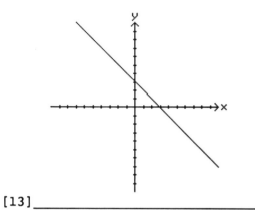

[13]

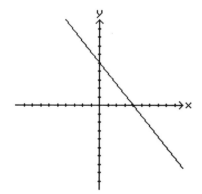

[14]

Key Sheet

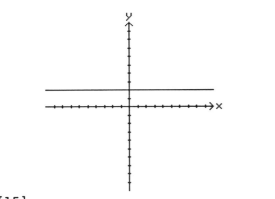

[15] _____

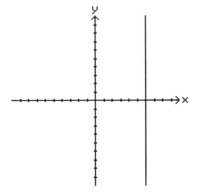

[16] _____

[17] $-\frac{1}{2}$ _____

[18] 2 _____

[19] no _____

Key Sheet

slope $= -\dfrac{9}{4}$

y-intercept $= \dfrac{5}{2}$

[20]_____

$y = -\dfrac{1}{5}x + 2$

[21]_____

[22] $x + 4y = 8$
_____

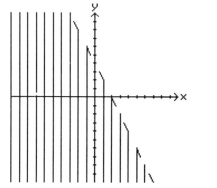

[23]_____

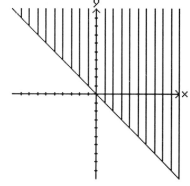

[24]_____

336

Key Sheet

---

[25] $23x + 38y \leq 76{,}000$

[26] $\$7.90$

Show your answers on the Student Answer Sheet.

---

1. Which system of equations has (-1, -3) as a solution?

   A)   x + y = -4   B)   x + y = -4
        x - y = 2   x - y = -2
   C)   2x + y = -5   D)   x + 2y = -7
        x - 2y = -7   2x - y = -5

2. Which system of equations has no solution?

   A)   2x - y = 5   B)   2x + y = 5
        4x - 2y = 7   4x - 2y = 7
   C)   2x - y = 5   D)   2x - y = 4
        4x + 2y = 10   4x - 2y = 8

3. Solve the system of equations.

   $3x - 5y = 6$

   $y = \frac{1}{5}$

   A) $(\frac{7}{3}, \frac{1}{5})$ B) $(2, \frac{1}{5})$

   C) $(\frac{1}{5}, \frac{27}{25})$ D) $(\frac{5}{3}, \frac{1}{5})$

4. Solve the system of equations.

   $\frac{1}{3}x + \frac{1}{6}y = \frac{2}{3}$

   $\frac{2}{5}x + \frac{1}{4}y = \frac{1}{5}$

   A) (-8, 12)   B) (8, -12)
   C) (6, -2)   D) (-6, 2)

5. The length of a rectangle is one centimeter less than three times the width. If the perimeter is 10 centimeters, find the width of the rectangle.

   A) 2.5 cm   B) 1.5 cm
   C) 0.5 cm   D) 3.5 cm

Show your answers on the Student Answer Sheet.

---

6. One number is one-fifth of another number. The sum of the two
    numbers is $\frac{4}{5}$. Find the larger of the two numbers.

    A) $\frac{2}{15}$ B) $\frac{3}{5}$

    C) $\frac{2}{3}$ D) $\frac{2}{5}$

7. The supply and demand equations for roasted cashews in Billings,
    Montana are the following:

    Supply: $p = 0.1x + 2.5$
    Demand: $p = -0.06x + 8.1$

    If p is the price per pound, in dollars, and x is the quantity, in
    thousands of pounds of cashews, find the equilibrium point.
    A) 35,000 lb   B) 15,000 lb
    C) 5,000 lb   D) 25,000 lb

8. A 10% acid solution is mixed with a 30% acid solution to make 80
    liters of a 15% acid solution. How many liters of the 10% acid
    solution are needed?
    A) 40 liters   B) 60 liters
    C) 30 liters   D) 20 liters

9. Determine if the ordered pair (-2, 3) is a solution of the
    system of equations.

    $x + 4y = 10$
    $-x - 3y = -4$

10. Graph the system of equations and find the solution.

    $x + y = -7$
    $x - y = -1$

11. Graph the system of equations and find the solution.

    $3x + 3y = 4$
    $-9x - 9y = -12$

12. Determine if the system of equations has one solution, no solution,
    or infinitely many solutions.

    $y = -x + 3$
    $y = 4x + 3$

Show your answers on the Student Answer Sheet.

13. Use the elimination method to solve the system of equations.

    4x - y = 6
    2x + y = 24

14. Use the elimination method to solve the system of equations.

    -2m - 4n = 4
     2m + 3n = -5

15. Use the elimination method to solve the system of equations.

    5x - 4y = 23
    -2x - y = -4

16. Use the elimination method to solve the system of equations.

    x + 6y = -1
    $\frac{2}{5}$x + $\frac{12}{5}$y = 7

17. Five times one number plus five times a second number is 0.
    The difference of the first number and the second number, divided
    by 3, is 2. Find the two numbers.

18. Use the substitution method to solve the system of equations.

    6m + 5n = -16
    n = -2m

19. Use the substitution method to solve the system of equations.

    x = -2y + 2
    4y + 2x = 4

20. Two angles are complementary. The measure of the larger angle is
    18° less than twice the measure of the smaller angle. Find the
    measure of the two angles.

21. Fivestar Corporation makes and sells x muffler systems each day with
    a total cost C, in dollars, given by C = 35x + 260. The corporation
    sells each system for $55.

    a) Express the daily revenue R in terms of x.
    b) Find the break-even point for the corporation.

22. A barge on a river can travel 256 miles down river in 8 hours and
    can travel the 256 miles up river in 16 hours. Find the rate of the
    barge in still water and the rate of the current.

Show your answers on the Student Answer Sheet.

23. Graph the system of inequalities.

    $6x - 5y \leq 30$
    $x \geq -1$

24. Graph the system of inequalities.

    $x + y < -3$
    $4x - 3y \geq 12$

Student Name _____ Score_____

Student Answer Sheet - Show all work. Use extra sheets if necessary.

[1]_____

[2]_____

[3]_____

[4]_____

[5]_____

[6]_____

[7]_____

[8]_____

[9]_____

Student Name _____ Score_____

Student Answer Sheet - Show all work.   Use extra sheets if necessary.

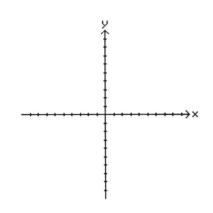

[10]_____

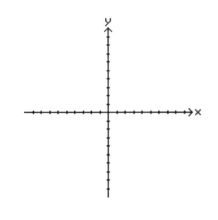

[11]_____

[12]_____

[13]_____

Student Name _____ Score_____

Student Answer Sheet – Show all work.   Use extra sheets if necessary.

[14] _____

[15] _____

[16] _____

[17] _____

[18] _____

[19] _____

[20] _____

[21] _____

[22] _____

Student Name _____ Score_____

Student Answer Sheet – Show all work. Use extra sheets if necessary.

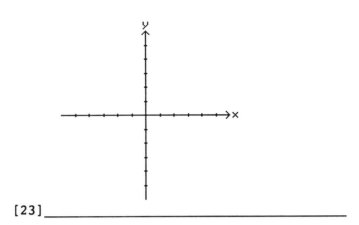

[23]_____

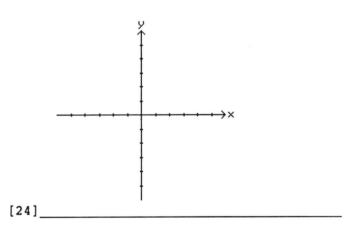

[24]_____

Key Sheet

[1] __A_____

[2] __A_____

[3] __A_____

[4] __B_____

[5] __B_____

[6] __C_____

[7] __A_____

[8] __B_____

[9] __no_____

Key Sheet

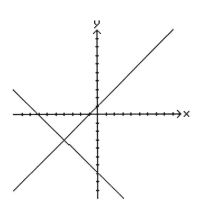

[10]___(-4, -3)_____

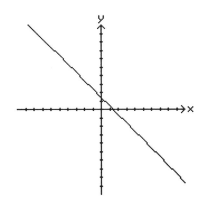

[11]___infinitely many solutions_____

[12]___one solution_____

[13]___x = 5 and y = 14_____

Key Sheet

[14] m = -4 and n = 1

[15] x = 3 and y = -2

[16] no solution

[17] 3 and -3

[18] m = 4 and n = -8

[19] infinitely many solutions

[20] 36° and 54°

[21] a) R = 55x
b) 13 muffler systems

[22] The barge travels 24 mph in still water
and the rate of the current is 8 mph.

Key Sheet

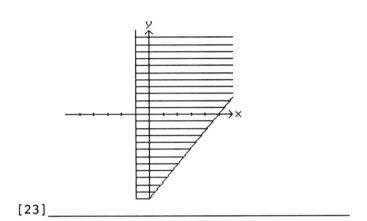

[23] _____

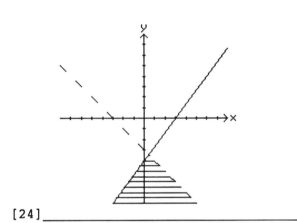

[24] _____

Show your answers on the Student Answer Sheet.

---

1. Which of the following is NOT a real number for $x = 2$?

   A) $\sqrt{x - 2}$ B) $\sqrt{x + 3}$

   C) $\sqrt{x - 3}$ D) $\sqrt{x + 2}$

2. Simplify $\dfrac{(x^{-3/2})^4}{(y^{4/3})^6}$

   A) $\dfrac{y^8}{x^6}$ B) $x^6 y^8$

   C) $\dfrac{x^6}{y^8}$ D) $\dfrac{1}{x^6 y^8}$

3. Find the value of $\sqrt{16 + 36}$.

   A) 10   B) $\sqrt{42}$

   C) $4\sqrt{52}$ D) $2\sqrt{13}$

4. Simplify $3\sqrt{5} + 6\sqrt{5}$.

   A) $18\sqrt{5}$ B) 45

   C) $9\sqrt{10}$ D) $9\sqrt{5}$

5. Simplify $\dfrac{7}{\sqrt{5}} - \dfrac{2}{\sqrt{5}}$.

   A) $\dfrac{1}{5}$ B) 5

   C) $5\sqrt{5}$ D) $\sqrt{5}$

Show your answers on the Student Answer Sheet.

---

6. Multiply $(\sqrt{5} + 1)$ by its conjugate and simplify the result.

   A) 4   B) $2\sqrt{5}$
   C) 6   D) $\sqrt{5} - 1$

7. Solve the equation: $x - 3 = \sqrt{x - 3}$

   A) $x = 4$ or $x = 3$ B) $x = 4$ or $x = 0$
   C) $x = 4$ D) $x = 3$

8. Find $(3 + 2i) - (4 - 7i)$.

   A) $12 - 14i$ B) $-1 + 9i$
   C) $7 - 5i$ D) $-1 - 5i$

9. Find the value.

   $-\sqrt[3]{\dfrac{64}{125}}$

10. Simplify the expression. Assume all variables are positive.

    $\sqrt{4c^2d^4f^8}$

11. Find the missing length of the right triangle.

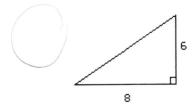

12. Find the value.

    $\left(\dfrac{16}{81}\right)^{2/4}$

13. Simplify and write the answer with only positive exponents.

    $6^{-5/3} \cdot 6^{7/3}$

Show your answers on the Student Answer Sheet.

14. Simplify and write the answer with only positive exponents.

$$\frac{(p^{-4/3})^6}{p^5}$$

15. Simplify.

$$\sqrt[4]{243s^3t^{10}u^{15}}$$

16. Simplify.

$$\sqrt{75}$$

17. Rationalize the denominator.

$$\frac{8f}{\sqrt{48f}}$$

18. Simplify by combining like radicals.

$$4\sqrt{7} - 3\sqrt{28} + \sqrt{14}$$

19. Simplify by combining like radicals.

$$2c\sqrt{c^3} - 2c^2\sqrt{c} + 3\sqrt{c^5}$$

20. Multiply and simplify.

$$(7\sqrt{2} - \sqrt{5})(\sqrt{2} + 3\sqrt{5})$$ $14 \;+20\sqrt{10}\; -15$

21. Rationalize the denominator and simplify.

$$\frac{3m}{\sqrt{m} + 9}$$ $\left(\dfrac{\sqrt{m}-9}{\sqrt{m}-9}\right) = \dfrac{3m\left(\sqrt{m}-9\right)}{m-81}$

22. Solve the equation.

$$\sqrt{s + 3} = 8$$

23. Solve the equation.

$$\sqrt{2j} + 4 = \sqrt{16 - 2j}$$

24. Express in the form a + bi.

$$6 - \sqrt{-16}$$

25. Divide and express in the form a + bi.

$$\frac{2 + 7i}{5 - 3i}$$

352     $\dfrac{MC}{2} \Big| \dfrac{No\ wt}{5}$

Student Name _____ Score_____

Student Answer Sheet - Show all work. Use extra sheets if necessary.

[1] _____

[2] _____

[3] _____

[4] _____

[5] _____

[6] _____

[7] _____

[8] _____

[9] _____

[10] _____

Student Name _____ Score_____

Student Answer Sheet - Show all work. Use extra sheets if necessary.

[11]_____

[12]_____

[13]_____

[14]_____

[15]_____

[16]_____

[17]_____

[18]_____

[19]_____

Student Name _____ Score_____

Student Answer Sheet - Show all work.   Use extra sheets if necessary.

[20]_____

[21]_____

[22]_____

[23]_____

[24]_____

[25]_____

Key Sheet

[1]   C

[2]   D

[3]   D

[4]   D

[5]   D

[6]   A

[7]   A

[8]   B

[9] $-\dfrac{4}{5}$

[10] $2cd^2f^4$

Key Sheet

[11] 10

[12] $\dfrac{4}{9}$

[13] $6^{2/3}$

[14] $\dfrac{1}{p^{13}}$

[15] $3t^2u^3\sqrt{3s^3t^2u^3}$

[16] $5\sqrt{3}$

[17] $\dfrac{2\sqrt{3f}}{3}$

[18] $\sqrt{14} - 2\sqrt{7}$

[19] $3c^2\sqrt{c}$

Key Sheet
---

[20] $-1 + 20\sqrt{10}$

[21] $\dfrac{3m\sqrt{m} - 27m}{m - 81}$

[22] $s = 61$

[23] $j = 0$

[24] $6 - 4i$

[25] $-\dfrac{11}{34} + \dfrac{41}{34}i$

Show your answers on the Student Answer Sheet.

---

1. Eight times a number squared is 56. Find the number.
   A) 7 or -7   B) 7
   C) $\sqrt{7}$ or $-\sqrt{7}$ D) $\sqrt{7}$

2. What term must be added to both sides of the equation
   $3x^2 + 5x + 7 = 0$ to solve by completing the square.

   A) $\dfrac{25}{9}$ B) $\dfrac{25}{36}$

   C) $\dfrac{25}{4}$ D) $\dfrac{25}{2}$

3. Write the equation $(x - 5)(2x + 7) = x + 6$ in the form
   $ax^2 + bx + c = 0$.

   A) $2x^2 - 2x - 30 = 0$ B) $2x^2 - 4x - 41 = 0$
   C) $2x^2 - 3x - 35 = 0$ D) $2x^2 - 4x - 30 = 0$

4. Which of the following is NOT a solution for the equation
   $x^3 - 4x^2 + 7x = 0$?

   A) 0   B) $2 - \sqrt{3}i$
   C) $-2 + \sqrt{3}$ D) $2 + \sqrt{3}i$

5. Which statement below best describes the nature and number of roots
   for the equation $3x^2 - 7x + 16 = 0$?
   A) two complex roots
   B) one real root
   C) two real roots
   D) one real root and one complex root

Show your answers on the Student Answer Sheet.

6. Solve the equation: $x^2 + 3x - 5 = 0$

A) $x = \dfrac{-3 + \sqrt{29}}{2}$ or $x = \dfrac{-3 - \sqrt{29}}{2}$

B) $x = \dfrac{3 + \sqrt{29}}{2}$ or $x = \dfrac{3 - \sqrt{29}}{2}$

C) $x = -3 + \dfrac{\sqrt{29}}{2}$ or $x = -3 - \dfrac{\sqrt{29}}{2}$

D) $x = \dfrac{-3 + \sqrt{11}}{2}$ or $x = \dfrac{-3 - \sqrt{11}}{2}$

7. Audiotronics Company makes and sells x entertainment centers each week. The daily cost C is given by $C = 5x^2 + 1500$ and the daily revenue R is given by $R = 200x$. The company cannot make more than 20 units per day. Find the break-even point for the company.

A) 18 units   B) 10 units
C) 15 units   D) 12 units

8. Which of the following describes the graph of the quadratic equation $y = -3(x + 5)^2 + 2$?

A) a parabola that opens downward with a vertex at (5, -2)
B) a parabola that opens upward with a vertex at (5, -2)
C) a parabola that opens upward with a vertex at (-5, 2)
D) a parabola that opens downward with a vertex at (-5, 2)

9. Solve the equation.

$(j + 1)^2 = 25$

10. Solve the equation.

$7a^2 = 3$

11. What constant must be added to $x^2 + \dfrac{9}{2}x$ to make a perfect square trinomial?

12. Solve the equation by completing the square.

$8s^2 - 2s = 1$

13. Solve the equation by using the quadratic formula.

$p^2 - 4p - 1 = 0$

14. Solve the equation.

$m(m - 4) = 1$

360

Show your answers on the Student Answer Sheet.

---

15. Solve the equation.

    $a^2 + 10 = 0$

16. Solve the equation.

    $x^2 + 4x = -31$

17. A projectile is launched from ground level. The height h, in meters, above the ground t seconds later is given by $h = 45t - 4.9t^2$. How far above the ground will the projectile be after 3 seconds?

18. The sum of a number and its reciprocal is $\frac{61}{30}$. Find the number.

19. Draw the graph of $y = \frac{1}{6}x^2$.

20. Draw the graph of $y = (x + 1)^2 + 3$.

21. Draw the graph of $y = x^2 - 3x - 1$.

22. Is the relation a function?
    $\{(-6, 1), (1, 7), (7, 3)\}$

23. Determine if the relation graphed below is a function.

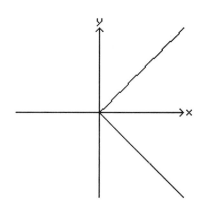

24. State the domain for the function.
    $y = \sqrt{x - 9}$

361

Show your answers on the Student Answer Sheet.

25. Let $f(x) = x^2 + 3x - 3$. Find $f(3)$.

Student Name _____ Score_____

Student Answer Sheet - Show all work. Use extra sheets if necessary.

[1]_____

[2]_____

[3]_____

[4]_____

[5]_____

[6]_____

[7]_____

[8]_____

[9]_____

[10]_____

Student Name _____ Score_____

Student Answer Sheet – Show all work. Use extra sheets if necessary.

[11]_____

[12]_____

[13]_____

[14]_____

[15]_____

[16]_____

[17]_____

[18]_____

Student Name _____ Score_____

Student Answer Sheet - Show all work. Use extra sheets if necessary.

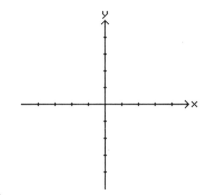

[19]_____

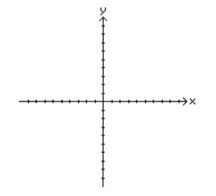

[20]_____

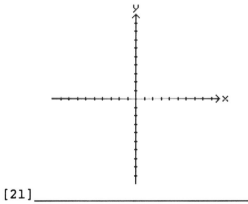

[21]_____

365

Student Name _____ Score_____

Student Answer Sheet - Show all work. Use extra sheets if necessary.

[22]_____

[23]_____

[24]_____

[25]_____

Key Sheet

[1]   C

[2]   B

[3]   B

[4]   C

[5]   A

[6]   A

[7]   B

[8]   D

[9]   4 or −6

[10] $\dfrac{\sqrt{21}}{7}$ or $-\dfrac{\sqrt{21}}{7}$

Key Sheet

[11] $\dfrac{81}{16}$

[12] $-\dfrac{1}{4}$ or $\dfrac{1}{2}$

[13] $2 + \sqrt{5}$ or $2 - \sqrt{5}$

[14] $2 + \sqrt{5}$ or $2 - \sqrt{5}$

[15] $\sqrt{10}i$ or $-\sqrt{10}i$

[16] $-2 + \sqrt{3}i$ or $-2 - \sqrt{3}i$

[17] 90.9 meters

[18] $\dfrac{5}{6}$ or $\dfrac{6}{5}$

Key Sheet

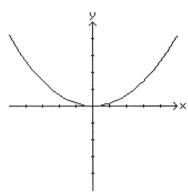

[19] _____

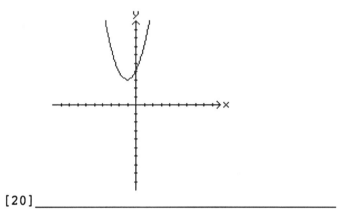

[20] _____

[21] _____

Key Sheet

[22] yes

[23] not a function

[24] $\{x : x \geq 9\}$

[25] 15